SCHOLASTIC

100
LITERACY HOMEWORK ACTIVITIES

- Stand-alone homework sheets
- Fits with any programme
- Easy to use

YEAR 4

Scottish Primary 5

Chris Webster

ACKNOWLEDGEMENTS

Published by Scholastic Ltd,
Villiers House,
Clarendon Avenue,
Leamington Spa,
Warwickshire CV32 5PR

© 2001 Scholastic Ltd.
New edition © 2006 Scholastic Ltd
Text © 2001, 2006 Chris Webster

Printed by Bell & Bain Ltd, Glasgow

2 3 4 5 6 7 8 9   7 8 9 0

AUTHORS
Chris Webster

EDITORIAL & DESIGN
Crystal Presentations Ltd

COVER DESIGN
Joy Monkhouse

ILLUSTRATOR
Garry Davies

British Library Cataloguing-in-Publication Data
A catalogue record for this book is available from the British Library.

ISBN 0-439-96587-X
ISBN 978-0439-96587-3

The publishers gratefully acknowledge permission to reproduce the following copyright material:

Extracts from the National Literacy Strategy reproduced under the terms of HMSO Guidance Note 8 © Crown copyright.

Every effort has been made to trace copyright holders. The publishers apologise for any inadvertent omissions.

100 Literacy Homework Activities: Year 4

100 Literacy Homework Activities: Year 4

Using the books

The activities in each book are organised by term, then by word-, sentence- and text-level focus and, finally, by specific National Literacy Strategy objective. Each of the 100 homework activities is comprised of at least one photocopiable page to send home. Each sheet provides instructions for the child and a brief note to the helper (be that a parent, grandparent, neighbour or sibling), stating simply and clearly its purpose and suggesting support and/ or a further challenge to offer the child. Every sheet is clearly marked with a W (word), S (sentence) or T (text) symbol to designate its main focus. (Please note that 'they', 'them', 'their' has sometimes been used in the helper and teachers' notes to refer to 'child'. This avoids the 'he or she' construction.)

Making the most of these resources

The best way to use these homework resources is to use them flexibly, integrating them with a sequence of literacy sessions over a number of days. Such an approach will also ensure that the needs of an individual, or groups of children, are met in different ways. Some of the homework sheets will be greatly enhanced by enlarging them to A3 size as this provides children with more space in which to write. Others, for example, the sets of story cards, lend themselves to being laminated for reuse.

Here are some ideas for different types of use:

Preparation
● Give a word- or sentence-level homework activity to prepare for a skills session later in the week. This allows the skill to be reviewed in less time, thus leaving more time for group activities.
● Give a text-level homework activity as a way of preparing for more detailed work on a particular type of text in a future literacy lesson.
● Give work on a particular short text as preparation for further work on that text, or a related text, in a future lesson.

Follow-up
● Give a word- or sentence-level homework activity as a follow-up to a literacy lesson to provide more practice in a particular skill.
● Give a text-level homework activity as a creative way of responding to work done in a literacy lesson.
● Use one of the many short texts as a follow-up to a study of a similar type of text in a lesson.

Reinforcement
● Give selected word- or sentence-level homework to specific children who need extra practice.
● Give a text-level homework activity to specific children to reinforce text-level work done in class.
● Use a short text with specific children to reinforce work done on similar texts.

Supporting your helpers

The importance of involving parents in homework is generally acknowledged. For this reason, as well as the 'Dear Helper' note on each homework sheet, there is also a homework diary sheet on page 128 which can be photocopied and sent home with the homework. Multiple copies of these can be filed or stapled together to make a longer-term homework record. For each activity, there is space to record its title, the date on which it was sent home and spaces for responses to the work from the helper, the child and the teacher. The homework diary is intended to encourage home-school links, so that parents and carers know what is being taught and can make informed comments about their child's progress. It is also worth writing to parents and helpers, or holding a meeting, to discuss their role. This could include an explanation of how they can support their children's homework, for example, by:
● providing a space where the child can concentrate and has the necessary resources to hand;
● becoming actively involved by interpreting instructions, helping with problems, sharing reading and participating in the paired activities where required.

Discuss with them how much time you expect the child to spend on the homework. If, after that time, a child is stuck, or has not finished, then suggest to the parent/helper that they should not force the child to continue. Ask them to write an explanation and the teacher will give extra help the next day. However, if children are succeeding at the task and need more time, this can be allowed – but bear in mind that children need a varied and balanced home life!

It is worth discussing with parents what is meant by 'help' as they should be careful that they do not go as far as doing the homework for the child. Legitimate help will include sharing the reading of texts, helping to clarify problems, discussing possible answers, etc, but it is important that the child is at some stage left to do his or her best. The teacher can then form an accurate assessment of the child's strengths and weaknesses and provide suitable follow-up work.

Using the activities with the All New 100 Literacy Hours series

A cross-referenced grid has been provided (on pages 5, 6 and 7) for those who wish to use these homework activities with the corresponding *All New 100 Literacy Hours* book. The grid suggests if and where a homework task might fit within the context of the appropriate *All New 100 Literacy Hours* unit and there may be more than one appropriate activity. Sometimes, the homework page could be used for a skills session in class and one of the resources from *All New 100 Literacy Hours* can be used for homework.

PAGE	HOMEWORK TITLE	USE AS A FOLLOW ON TO:	NLS OBJECTIVE LINK	LINK TO 100 LITERACY HOURS
27	Long vowels	Looking at long vowel phonemes	Y4 T1 W1	
28	Hoping and hopping	Spelling two-syllable words with double consonants	Y4 T1 W5	Unit 1 Hour 1
29	Double trouble	Spelling two-syllable words with double consonants	Y4 T1 W5	Unit 1 Hour 4
30	I see the sea	Following up on work on homophones	Y4 T1 W6	Unit 1 Hour 3
31	Tense tables	Spelling regular and irregular verb endings	Y4 T1 W7/8	Unit 3 Hour 5 Unit 5 Hour 7
32	Abstract nouns	Recognising and spelling suffixes 'ship', 'hood', 'ness'	Y4 T1 W9	
33	Phantom pharaohs	Using third/fourth place letters to order words alphabetically	Y4 T1 W12/11	Unit 3 Hour 4 Unit 5 Hour 3
34	Silly Billy	Exploring rhyming poetry	Y4 T1 W13	
35	Verbalise it!	Turning nouns and adjectives into verbs	Y4 T1 W14	
36	Present tense	Investigating verb tenses: present tense	Y4 T1 S2	Unit 1 Hour 5 Unit 3 Hour 1
37	Past tense	Investigating verb tenses: past tense	Y4 T1 S2	Unit 1 Hour 2 Unit 4 Hour 4
38	Future tense	Investigating verb tenses: future tense	Y4 T1 S2	Unit 5 Hour 10
39	Be kind, please rewind	Investigating verb tenses: imperative mood	Y4 T1 S2	Unit 6 Hour 3, 5
40	Budgie's big day	Comparing tenses of sentences	Y4 T1 S2	Unit 5 Hour 10 Unit 4 Hour 4; Unit 1 Hour 2
41	Crocodile river	Focusing on powerful verbs	Y4 T1 S3	Unit 1 Hour 2; Unit 2 Hour 1, 3, 5 Unit 3 Hour 2, 3, 5
42	Quickly	Identifying common adverbs ending in 'ly'	Y4 T1 S4	Unit 3 Hour 1 Unit 1 Hour 2, 5
43	Horoscope adverbs	Using adverbs to write about characters	Y4 T1 S4	Unit 1 Hour 2, 5 Unit 3 Hour 1
44	Cluttered desk	Using commas to separate items in a list	Y4 T1 S5	
45	Character quotes	Studying characters in a story	Y4 T1 T2	Unit 2 Hour 2, 3
46	Story order	Preparing to plan a story/exploring narrative order	Y4 T1 T4	Unit 1 Hour 3–5
47	All in good time	Performing a playscript	Y4 T1 T5	Unit 4
48	Two eagle poems	Comparing and contrasting two poems on similar themes	Y4 T1 T7	
49	Poem v poem	Comparing and contrasting two poems on similar themes	Y4 T1 T7	Unit 3 Hour 2
50	Dinosaur plateau	Preparing to write a story	Y4 T1 T9	Unit 1 Hour 3, 4
51	Pantomime planner	Writing a playscript based on a known story	Y4 T1 T13	Unit 4 Hour 1–3
52	Monty mouse	Using paragraphs to organise and sequence narrative	Y4 T1 T15	Unit 1 Hour 4/5
53	The resort of the millennium	Identifying features of non-fiction texts which support information retrieval	Y4 T1 T17	Unit 5 Hour 8/9
54	A loaded gun?	Distinguishing between fact and opinion	Y4 T1 T19	Unit 5 Hour 3, 4, 9
55	Porto Paso times	Identifying the main features of newspapers	Y4 T1 T20	Unit 5 Hour 8
56	Newspaper features	Identifying the main features of newspapers	Y4 T1 T20	Unit 5 Hour 10
57	Headline news	Using headlines to predict newspaper stories	Y4 T1 T21	Unit 5 Hour 3
58	Easy-tent	Identifying features of instructions	Y4 T1 T22	Unit 6
59	Be a newspaper editor	Editing a newspaper story to fit a given space	Y4 T1 T24	Unit 5 Hour 2, 5 Unit 7 Hour 3, 5
60	Driving guide	Preparing to write instructions	Y4 T1 T25	Unit 6 Hour 1
61	Porto Paso report	Looking at report writing	Y4 T1 T27	Unit 7 Hour 3–5

PAGE	HOMEWORK TITLE	USE AS A FOLLOW ON TO:	NLS OBJECTIVE LINK	LINK TO 100 LITERACY HOURS
62	Chefs and chiefs	Looking at the spelling of plurals	Y4 T2 W5	
63	Damsel in distress	Spelling words with common endings 'ight' and 'ite'	Y4 T2 W6	Unit 3 Hour 1, 3
64	Got a nice garden	Improving writing by substituting more effective words	Y4 T2 W9	Unit 2 Hour 4
65	Where's my partner?	Discussing words which use the suffix 'ess' to suggest gender	Y4 T2 W10	
66	Who's my partner?	Discussing words which use the suffix 'ess' to suggest gender	Y4 T2 W10	
67	Arseling-pole	Looking at how words change over time	Y4 T2 W11	Unit 3 Hour 3
68	Glossary	Looking at how words change over time	Y4 T2 W11	Unit 3 Hour 3
69	Enjoyable, delightful, childlike	Adding suffixes to nouns and verbs to make adjectives	Y4 T2 W13	
70	Shocking, dynamic, newsworthy!	Adding suffixes to nouns and verbs to make adjectives	Y4 T2 W13	
71	Fussy werewolf	Revising knowledge about adjectives	Y4 T2 S1	Unit 1 Hour 1, 2
72	Horoscope adjectives	Preparing to create or write about characters using adjectives	Y4 T2 S1	Unit 1 Hour 1, 2
73	Carry my case	Examining adjectives used for comparison	Y4 T2 S1	Unit 1 Hour 4
74	Oddly shaped	Looking at adjectival phrases in preparation for story writing	Y4 T2 S1	Unit 1 Hour 3
75	Jason's lipstick	Reinforcing the use of the possessive apostrophe	Y4 T2 S2	Unit 2
76	Cat o' nine tails	Distinguishing between apostrophe for contraction and possession	Y4 T2 S2	Unit 2 Hour 3–5
77	Imaginary worlds	Preparing to write a story based on an imaginary world	Y4 T2 T1	Unit 1 Hour 1
78	Alien in the mall	Understanding how settings influence events and incidents in stories	Y4 T2 T2	Unit 1 Hour 2
79	Land of snow-capped mountains	Comparing and contrasting story settings	Y4 T2 T3	Unit 1 Hour 5
80	See, saw, stegosaur	Looking at similes	Y4 T2 T5	Unit 3 Hour 1
81	Robin and Gandelyn	Investigating archaic language in poetry	Y4 T2 T6	Unit 3 Hour 3
82	Lots of legs	Exploring different rhyming patterns in poetry	Y4 T2 T7	Unit 3 Hour 1, 3
83	The creature of Croglin	Identifying different rhyming patterns in poetry	Y4 T2 T7	Unit 3 Hour 1, 3
84	Knitting needle database	Reviewing a range of stories	Y4 T2 T8	Unit 2 Hour 4
85	School setting	Using a plan to create a story setting	Y4 T2 T10	Unit 1 Hour 4
86	Alien planet	Using images as prompts to explore story settings	Y4 T2 T10	Unit 1 Hour 4, 5
87	Whale	Writing a poem based on the structure of an existing poem	Y4 T2 T11	Unit 3 Hour 4
88	Stonehenge	Selecting information from a text	Y4 T2 T14	Unit 4 Hour 1
89	Non-fiction review	Evaluating non-fiction books for a research task	Y4 T2 T15	Unit 4 Hour 3, 6
90	Armour	Selecting key headings, words or sentences for research	Y4 T2 T18	Unit 4 Hour 5–10
91	Flying machines	Preparing to write non-fiction by looking at organisation of texts	Y4 T2 T19	Unit 5 Hour 1
92	Legend or history?	Turning notes into connected prose	NL4 T2 T22	Unit 4 Hour 9
93	Arena	Collecting information from a variety of sources	Y4 T2 T23	Unit 4 Hour 10
94	Flushed with success	Redrafting an explanation using connectives	Y4T 2T 24	Unit 5 Hour 1
95	Engine	Preparing to write an explanation	Y4 T2 T25	Unit 5 Hour 4–5

PAGE	HOMEWORK TITLE	USE AS A FOLLOW ON TO:	NLS OBJECTIVE LINK	LINK TO 100 LITERACY HOURS
96	SS	Exploring the letter string 'ss'	Y4 T3 W5	
97	From aqua to aquarium	Reading a text that contains words based on Latin roots	Y4 T3 W7	
98	Boy overboard	Investigating homophones or similar sounding words	Y4 T3 W8	Unit 4 Hour 5
99	Possible...and probable!	Recognising and spelling suffixes 'ible' and 'able'	Y4 T3 W9	
100	Commotion and confusion	Recognising and spelling suffixes 'tion and 'sion'	Y4 T3 W9	
101	Is it its?	Distinguishing between its and it's	Y4 T3 W10	Unit 4 Hour 4
102	Baby bank	Investigating compound words	Y4 T3 W11	
103	Big and little	Reading a text containing diminutives	Y4 T3 W12	Unit 4 Hour 3
104	Oh dash!	Looking at punctuation/preparing to write	Y4 T3 S2	Unit 3 Hour 3–5
105	Mandy's studio	Looking at punctuation/preparing to write	Y4 T3 S2	Unit 3 Hour 3–5
106	Turn it down!	Investigating different types of sentence	Y4 T3 S4	Unit 3 Hour 1, 2 Unit 4 Hour 7
107	Only connect	Preparing to write an argument by looking at connectives	Y4 T3 S4	Unit 5 Hour 1–5 Unit 6 Hour 5
108	Bina's betrothal	Reading a text that raises cultural issues	Y4 T3 T1	Unit 2 Hour 1 Unit 3 Hour 1
109	Banja's coming of age	Examining similarities and differences between stories about cultural issues	Y4 T3 T2	Unit 4 Hour 1–5
110	The death of Robin Hood	Looking at terms such as verse, chorus, couple, rhyme, rhythm, alliteration	Y4 T3 T4	Unit 1 Hour 1–3
111	Haiku	Counting syllables in poetry	Y4 T3 T5	Unit 1 Hour 1
112	Lucky dog!	Counting syllables in poetry	Y4 T3 T5	Unit 1 Hour 1
113	Old lady from China	Writing about a poem by focusing on poetic techniques and personal response	Y4 T3 T6	Unit 1 Hour 1, 3
114	Dracula?	Studying poetic techniques/preparing to write a poem	Y4 T3 T6	Unit 1 Hour 3
115	Mnemonic rhymes	Exploring different kinds of verse	Y4 T3 T7	Unit 1
116	Death by water	Preparing to study a longer text which addresses an issue	Y4 T3 T8	Unit 3 Hour 1
117	Lost wallet	Preparing to study a longer text which addresses an issue. Suitable as an alternative to 116 for less able children	Y4 T3 T8	Unit 3 Hour 1
118/9	Are you a bookworm?	Reflecting on reading habits	Y4 T3 T10	
120	Skyliner complaint	Reading and evaluating arguments	Y4 T3 T16	Unit 5 Hour 1, 3
121	Unsafe at any speed	Examining how arguments are presented	Y4 T3 T17	Unit 5 Hour 1, 3
122	Skyliner	Evaluating adverts for impact and honesty	Y4 T3 T19	Unit 6 Hour 3, 4
123	Skyliner postcard	Summarising a text	Y4 T3 T20	Unit 5 Hour 2
124	R101	Summarising a text	Y4 T3 T20	Unit 5 Hour 2, 4
125	Five-point plan	Planning a persuasion or argument by sequencing the points	Y4 T3 T21	Unit 5
126	Aviation biographies	Summarising the key points in a non-fiction text	Y4 T3 T24	Unit 2 Hour 2 Unit 3 Hour 3
127	The Phantom of the Opera	Summarising the key points from a piece of classic fiction	Y4 T3 T24	Unit 2 Hour 2 Unit 3 Hour 3

Teachers' notes

TERM 1

p27 LONG VOWELS

Objective
Read and spell words through identifying phonemes.
(Y4, T1, W1)

Lesson context
Any lesson in which spelling is a focus.

Setting the homework
Revise the term *vowel*. The homework focuses on long vowels. The long sound is the name of the letter: 'bay', 'see', 'pile', 'cone', 'tune'. Long vowel phonemes can be spelled in many different ways. Explain to the children that they should think of their own examples.

Differentiation
Less able children should be encouraged to find as many as they can. More able children could be asked to think of several examples and use them in sentences..

Back at school
Share all the examples. Write them on the board. This will be helpful to any less able children who may have left gaps.

p28 HOPING AND HOPPING

Objective
Spell two-syllable words containing double consonants.
(Y4, T1, W5)

Lesson context
Reading text with words with double consonants or spelling work on two-syllable words with double consonants.

Setting the homework
Revise the term *consonant*. Go over the explanation. The first part is about one of the purposes of double consonants, the second is a spelling rule for adding suffixes.

Differentiation
None is needed, particularly if less able children are encouraged to work with a helper.

Back at school
Complete the table with the children. Monitor their spellings.

p29 DOUBLE TROUBLE

Objective
Spell two-syllable words containing double consonants.
(Y4, T1, W5)

Lesson context
Reading text with words with double consonants or spelling work on two-syllable words with double consonants. It would also be a useful follow-up to page 28, 'Hoping and hopping'.

Setting the homework
Explain that the poem contains the rules for using double consonants. But, of course, there are exceptions to the rules! The children have to pick out the rules and write them in prose.

Differentiation
This page is for more able children.

Back at school
Use as a whole-class activity to revise the double consonant spelling rules.

p30 I SEE THE SEA

Objective
Distinguish between the spellings and meanings of common homophones. (Y4, T1, W6)

Lesson context
Follow-up to work on homophones, as preparation for written work, or for any child who has confused one or more of these homophones.

Setting the homework
Point out that homophones have a valuable purpose: the different spellings help avoid confusion about meaning.

Differentiation
Children who make mistakes after this homework should be given more practice.

Back at school
Monitor mistakes caused by confusion about homophones in children's written work.

p31 TENSE TABLES

Objective
Spell regular and irregular verb endings. (Y4, T1, W7/8)

Lesson context
Could be part of a series of lessons on verbs. See also pages 36–40.

Setting the homework
Revise the definitions. Warn children that, for some words, they will need to apply additional spelling rules, (eg dropping silent e or doubling a consonant when adding -ing; adding -es rather than just -s).

Differentiation
Children who are uncertain about two or more terms in the explanatory text should be given work to help them understand.

Back at school
Complete the table with the children.

p32 ABSTRACT NOUNS

Objective
Recognise and spell suffixes: -ship, -hood, -ness.
(Y4, T1, W9)

Lesson context
Use with any text containing examples of these suffixes, or as part of a series of lessons on different types of noun.

Setting the homework
Revise the term *noun*. Brainstorm the names of things and then the names of some abstract ideas, eg 'love', so that the difference between concrete and abstract nouns can be explored.

Differentiation
Less able children may be able to *say* the abstract nouns but have trouble writing them. Helpers will be able to assist with this.

Back at school
Go over the abstract nouns in the second column while children mark their own.

p33 PHANTOM PHARAOHS

Objective
Use third and fourth place letters to place words in alphabetical order and define familiar vocabulary in their own words. (Y4, T1, W12/11)

Lesson context
Good preparation for a research task involving the use of indexes, glossaries, dictionaries or encyclopaedias.

Setting the homework
Emphasise that the skill is knowing your alphabet. Explain the principle of using second, third, fourth place (etc.) letters. Explain that the children should think of their own definitions first. If they do not know a word, they can look it up in a dictionary, but they must write the definition using their words.

Differentiation
Children who are still vague about the alphabet should be given basic work alphabetising by first letters.

Back at school
Display an OHP of the sorted list so children can check their alphabetical order. Discuss the definitions. A follow-up would be to write an alliterative poem or story using some of the words.

p34 SILLY BILLY

Objective
Use a rhyming dictionary. (Y4, T1, W13)

Lesson context
Part of a series of lessons exploring different kinds of poems or as follow-up to a lesson on rhyming poetry.

Setting the homework
Explain that a rhyming dictionary can do more than just suggest rhymes; it can suggest an idea which can be used to develop a poem.

Differentiation
Less able children could be given the first rhyme for each of the two verses: verse 2 = 'free'; last verse = 'away'. They could also be asked to write rhyming couplets instead of ballad verses.

Back at school
Discuss how the children used the extracts from the rhyming dictionary. Encourage them to explore rhyme further.

p35 VERBALISE IT!

Objective
Explore the ways in which nouns and adjectives can be made into verbs. (Y4, T1, W14)

Lesson context
This homework could be used as part of a study of parts of speech or of spelling patterns.

Setting the homework
Explain that nouns and adjectives can be changed into verbs by following certain patterns. Explain that the task is to match the nouns and adjectives to the verbs, then look for patterns in the way the words have been changed.

Differentiation
More able children could be asked to distinguish between nouns and adjectives in column 1.

Back at school
Emphasise the patterns of changes that children have found.

p36 PRESENT TENSE

Objective
Investigate verb tenses: present tense. (Y4, T1, S2)

Lesson context
Use as part of a series of lessons on verbs (see also pages 31, 37–40).

Setting the homework
This activity revises the simple present tense and introduces the present continuous tense. Ensure that children understand the terms for the different tenses and what they are used for. Explain how verb tables work, and revise the terms *singular*, *plural* and *person*.

Differentiation
Some children should write verb tables for the simple present tense only.

Back at school
Verb table blanks on OHT are a good way to involve children in reporting back.

p37 PAST TENSE

Objective
Investigate verb tenses: past tense. (Y4, T1, S2)

Lesson context
Use as part of a series of lessons on verbs (see also pages 31, 36, 38–40).

Setting the homework
This activity revises the simple past tense and introduces the past continuous tense. Ensure that children understand the terms for the different tenses and what they are used for. Explain how verb tables work, and revise the terms *singular*, *plural* and *person*.

Differentiation
Some children should write verb tables for the simple past tense only.

Back at school
Verb table blanks on OHT are a good way to involve children in reporting back.

p38 FUTURE TENSE

Objective
Investigate verb tenses: future tense. (Y4, T1, S2)

Lesson context
Use as part of a series of lessons on verbs (see also pages 31, 36–37, 39–40).

Setting the homework
The future tense is formed using the auxiliary verb 'will'. Ensure that children understand the terms for the different tenses and what the tenses are used for. Explain how verb tables work, and revise the terms *singular*, *plural* and *person*.

Differentiation
Some children should write verb tables for the future tense using the auxiliary verb 'will' only.

Back at school
Verb table blanks on OHT are a good way to involve children in reporting back.

p39 BE KIND, PLEASE REWIND

Objective
Investigate verb tenses: imperative mood. (Y4, T1, S2)

Lesson context
Use as part of a series of lessons on verbs (see also pages 31, 36–38, 40) or as preparation for reading or writing instructions.

Setting the homework
NOTE: *Imperative mood* is the correct term, though this is not used in the National Literacy Framework. Ensure that children understand how the imperative mood of the verb is formed and what it means.

Differentiation
Some children may have difficulty identifying the imperative verbs that are not at the beginning of sentences. However, encourage all children to attempt all ten questions.

Back at school
Apply the knowledge of the imperative mood to reading or writing tasks based on instructions.

p40 BUDGIE'S BIG DAY

Objective
Compare the tenses used in sentences from narrative and information texts. (Y4, T1, S2)

Lesson context
Use as part of a series of lessons on verbs (see also pages 31, 36–39).

Setting the homework
Explain that the types of texts are: a story, a diary entry, instructions, an information text, a persuasive text.

Differentiation
Give less able children versions of the page which have the type of text already printed in. The more able could be asked to distinguish between simple and continuous tenses.

Back at school
Discuss the types of text and how tenses are used in each one: 'Stories' – past tense; 'diaries' – all three; 'instructions' – imperative mood; 'persuasive texts' – mainly in the present tense; 'information texts' – past and present tenses.

p41 CROCODILE RIVER

Objective
Identify the use of powerful verbs through cloze procedure. (Y4, T1, S3)

Lesson context
Good preparation for creative writing or as part of the process of redrafting a story.

Setting the homework
Use the example to explain how some verbs are more powerful than others in specific contexts. Often, the verb that first comes to mind simply describes the action. Ask children to double check that the words they have used to fill the gaps are *verbs*.

Differentiation
All children should attempt this task.

Back at school
Share the different words used and 'weigh' each one to discuss its power and effectiveness.

p42 QUICKLY

Objective
Identify common adverbs with an *-ly* suffix. (Y4, T1, S4)

Lesson context
Use in a study of parts of speech or to enhance a piece of creative writing.

Setting the homework
Revise the meaning of the term *adverb* using the explanation on the page.

Differentiation
A full understanding of all the different kinds of adverbs (time, place, manner, degree) is difficult, but common *-ly* adverbs are easy to use and identify because of the *-ly* ending.

Back at school
Discuss the different adjectives that children used and check that they found all the adverbs. If the 'Lesson context' was creative writing, encourage children to redraft their writing by finding if an adverb would improve the description.

p43 HOROSCOPE ADVERBS

Objective
Use adverbs with greater discrimination in own writing. (Y4, T1, S4)

Lesson context
Use in a study of adverbs, writing about characters in literature, or creating own characters for stories. Note that it can be 'twinned' with page 72, 'Horoscope adjectives' (Term 2).

Setting the homework
NOTE: Children who belong to certain religious groups may feel more comfortable if the lists of adverbs are disassociated from signs of the zodiac. Children should be told which aspect of the second task to focus on. If they are studying a novel, they could choose three adverbs to describe each character. If they are writing a story, they should choose three adverbs for each character in their story.

Differentiation
The meanings of a few of the adverbs may need explaining to some less able children.

Back at school
Apply the chosen adverbs to the context of the lesson.

p44 CLUTTERED DESK

Objective
Practise using commas within sentences. (Y4, T1, S5)

Lesson context
It is not helpful to teach that a comma marks a pause in a sentence. The best approach is to teach a series of specific uses of the comma, eg in lists, in dialogue, to mark appositive phrases, to mark clause divisions.

Setting the homework
Note that children will sometimes find commas used before 'and'. Explain that a comma is used before 'and' if the writer wants to emphasise the last item.

Differentiation
More able children could be asked to make up a number of additional lists.

Back at school
Go over the homework. Remember to allow for differences of interpretation of the pictures. The main thing is that the sequence of commas and 'and' should be correct.

p45 CHARACTER QUOTES

Objective
Identify the main characteristics of key characters, drawing on the text to justify views. (Y4, T1, T2)

Lesson context
The study of characters in a story. This homework is a step towards the writing of essays which use quotations from the text to support key points.

Setting the homework
Enough of the story needs to have been read so there is plenty of evidence about character.

Differentiation
All children can attempt this homework. Less able children will be helped by being given page numbers to refer to for each section.

Back at school
Share descriptions of different aspects of the character or characters, and the evidence chosen to support it. The next step is to write out the information in essay form.

p46 STORY ORDER

Objective
Explore narrative order. (Y4, T1, T4)

Lesson context
A good preparation for planning a story. It will help children learn how to divide a story into paragraphs. The story itself can be used to help less able children write a story in response to page 50, 'Dinosaur plateau'. Note that this is the first of several homework activities based on the imaginary city of Porto Paso. The others can be found on pages 50, 53, 55–57, 59 and 61.

Setting the homework
Remind the children that a story must have a beginning, middle and end and that this model divides the middle into three sections: build up, conflict and climax.

Differentiation
The more able could add two or three more paragraphs to the 'conflict' section. Each paragraph should deal with a different adventure.

Back at school
Share ideas on what other adventures could be added to the 'conflict' section. Children who wrote additional paragraphs could read them out at this stage.

p47 ALL IN GOOD TIME

Objective
Prepare, read and perform a playscript. (Y4, T1, T5)

Lesson context
The playscript can be used as practice for preparing a longer play in class, or be extended into a playscript for performance. The page is also useful as a model for writing playscripts, eg when using page 51, 'Pantomime planner'.

Setting the homework
Ask children to read the play with their helper first and then discuss how it could be prepared for performance. Ask them to think about the following: casting, staging, props, acting, movement.

Differentiation
Less able children need not write the extra scene. They could think of an idea.

Back at school
Discuss ideas for the performance and for extra scenes, and ask for volunteers to read out examples. Transfer the skills to another, longer play, or extend the playscript by adding some of the best extra scenes.

p48 TWO EAGLE POEMS

Objective
Compare and contrast poems on similar themes. (Y4, T1, T7)

Lesson context
This homework compares a classic and a modern poem about eagles. It would make a good follow-up to a lesson in which a number of animal poems had been studied, or poems written in different verse forms.

Setting the homework
If this is a follow-up to similar work done in class, children will know what to look for when comparing and contrasting poems. For example, the NLS Framework asks them to consider: form, language, personal responses and preferences.

Differentiation
Less able children will benefit from the support of the template on page 49, 'Poem v poem'. The more able will benefit from considering the poems by themselves.

Back at school
Share ideas about the similarities and differences between these two poems. Children could write their own eagle poems.

p49 POEM V POEM

Objective
Compare and contrast poems on similar themes. (Y4, T1, T7)

Lesson context
This writing frame can be used when comparing any two poems with the same themes.

Setting the homework
If possible, enlarge the page to A3 size to allow space for writing. Revise the terminology used, eg *rhymed verse*, *free verse*, *rhythm*, *simile*, *metaphor*. Either give this page along with page 48, or provide the children with two poems with a similar theme to compare and contrast.

Differentiation
For some children, simplify the frame, asking only one question in each section.

Back at school
Discuss the similarities and differences between these poems. Use the template as a guide to reworking the ideas into essay form as a whole-class activity.

p50 DINOSAUR PLATEAU

Objective
Use different ways of planning stories. (Y4, T1, T9)

Lesson context
Preparation for story writing. This homework page is the second of a series of pages based on the imaginary city of Porto Paso. See also pages 46, 53, 55–57, 59 and 61. These pages can be used together to provide the stimulus for a range of writing for different purposes.

Setting the homework
Recap on the basics of story structure (see page 46, 'Story order'), and explain that this map provides support for planning a well-structured story. The beginning and end are well defined, and the middle sections can be developed from the many hazards.

Differentiation
Less able children could develop the outline story on page 46. This outline could be developed by planning two or three more exciting incidents after the attack by bandits.

Back at school
Children can share and comment on each others' plans. Ask them to refine their plans and begin writing.

p51 PANTOMIME PLANNER

Objective
Write playscripts using known stories as a basis. (Y4, T1, T13)

Lesson context
Use in the context of writing a playscript, or the pantomime idea can be further developed in class.

Setting the homework
The idea is to stimulate ideas for the playscript of a pantomime which should be modern and different from the traditional pantomime.

Differentiation
Children of all abilities will be able to contribute imaginative ideas.

Back at school
When writing the final draft of the playscript ensure that the appropriate conventions are followed. This can be done by using the script on page 47, 'All in good time' as a model.

p52 MONTY MOUSE

Objective
Use paragraphs in story writing to organise and sequence the narrative. (Y4, T1, T15)

Lesson context
Preparing to write a story.

Setting the homework
Revise the paragraphing explanation. Add that a paragraph is a group of sentences on one topic, or in a story, about one scene. Revise the terms *indent* and *indentation*, and point out that the first paragraph is not indented. Explain how important it is to go 'back to the margin' on the lines following the indented line. Finally, explain the writing frame.

Differentiation
More able children could adapt the writing frame, by adding paragraphs and using different ways of starting them.

Back at school
Either apply the paragraphing skills to another story, or develop the story.

p53 THE RESORT OF THE MILLENNIUM

Objective
Identify features of non-fiction texts which support the reader in gaining information efficiently. (Y4, T1, T17)

Lesson context
The homework is a non-fiction text in the form of a magazine article about Porto Paso. It can be used as an example of 'signposting' in non-fiction in preparation for researching a topic or as reference material for other work on Porto Paso (see page 61, 'Porto Paso report'). Other pages dealing with the imaginary city of Porto Paso are 46, 50, 55–57, 59 and 61.

Setting the homework
Explain the task. A helpful way to answer the second question is to compare this kind of text with a text that is just words, ie, no headings etc.

Back at school
Display the different examples of non-fiction texts brought in and discuss their signposting.

p54 A LOADED GUN?

Objective
Understand the terms *fact* and *opinion* and distinguish the two in reading and other media. (Y4, T1, T19)

Lesson context
This is good preparation for studying other persuasive texts. Alternatively, it could be used as the starting point for an investigation into types of argument, research into the effects of smoking, writing a persuasive essay, and/or designing an anti-smoking campaign.

Setting the homework
Define *fact* and *opinion*. Use the first three sentences to explain the difference.

Differentiation
Less able children should find the facts first. They should also be able to find some of the more obvious opinions. The more able should be able to find the opinions which are less obvious.

Back at school
Highlight fact and opinion during a follow-up discussion. The lesson can then be developed, or the skills transferred to another topic.

p55 PORTO PASO TIMES

Objective
Identify the main features of newspapers. (Y4, T1, T20)

Lesson context
This homework focuses on the features of newspapers and can be used as a preparation for a lesson on newspapers or on non-fiction texts. It is part of the series of activities based on the imaginary city of Porto Paso. See also pages 46, 50, 53, 56–57, 59 and 61.

Setting the homework
This is a simulated newspaper front page. To preserve the authenticity of the simulation, no pupil task or helper notes have been included. This should be written on the board for children to copy: TASK: Highlight examples of headlines, subheadings, columns, captions, bullet points. List the range of information (refer to the contents at the top of the page as well as the page itself). DEAR HELPER: Help your child to find examples of these features in a 'real' newspaper.

Back at school
Discuss the features found in this and other newspapers that children looked at.

p56 NEWSPAPER FEATURES

Objective
Identify the main features of newspapers. (Y4, T1, T20)

Lesson context
This focuses on the features of newspapers and can be used to take the previous lesson further by analysing the features of two different newspapers.

Setting the homework
Ask parents to provide two newspapers which are as different as possible. If this is likely to be a problem, the previous page can be used as one of the newspapers. Enlarge this homework page to A3 size to allow more space for writing.

Differentiation
Some less able children could be asked to focus on the first two sections only.

Back at school
Discuss the comparisons between different newspapers.

p57 HEADLINE NEWS

Objective
Predict newspaper stories from the evidence of headlines.
(Y4, T1, T21)

Lesson context
This focuses on headlines, but children will need background information to predict the articles. Page 53, 'The resort of the millennium', provides this information and should be given out with this page. Other pages in the series on Porto Paso are 46, 50, 53, 55–56, 59 and 61.

Setting the homework
Explain to children that they can write anything under the headlines as long as it does not contradict the basic information in the article 'The resort of the millenium'.

Back at school
Children should evaluate each other's articles on two criteria only – does the article: a) fit the headline; b) fit the information on page 53? Discuss the grammar of headlines – they are 'telegraphic', ie some words are left out.

p58 EASY-TENT

Objective
Identify the features of instructions. (Y4, T1, T22)

Lesson context
Use as a follow-up to or preparation for a lesson on reading or writing instructions, or on the imperative mood. See also page 39, 'Be kind, please rewind', which focuses on the imperative mood.

Setting the homework
Discuss instructions which children have used. Ask: *Have they ever been frustrated by instructions which were not clear?* Go over the features listed and explain that the task is to find and highlight them. Revise the imperative mood.

Differentiation
Less able children who are still struggling with verbs should omit this part of the task.

Back at school
Ask the children to swap instructions and say if they could follow them without getting confused.

p59 BE A NEWSPAPER EDITOR

Objective
Edit newspaper stories to fit a particular space.
(Y4, T1, T24)

Lesson context
This focuses on editing a text to fit a given space and can be used as a practice task to prepare children for editing a magazine or newspaper, or as an exercise in summarizing skills. This activity is part of the series on the imaginary city of Porto Paso. See also pages 46, 50, 53, 55–57 and 61.

Setting the homework
Go over the task and the suggestions. Explain that, as the editor, it is their decision how to shorten the article. The main decision will be whether to leave out whole sections, or to try to keep everything in, though in a shorter form. Ask the children to count the number of words in their final version.

Differentiation
Less able children should cut whole sections rather than try to summarise it.

Back at school
Discuss the task and different possible solutions to it.

p60 DRIVING GUIDE

Objective
Write clear instructions using conventions learned from reading.
(Y4, T1, T25)

Lesson context
Use as a preparation for writing instructions. Link with other work on instructions and the imperative mood (see also page 39, 'Be kind, please rewind', which focuses on the imperative mood, and page 58, 'Easy-tent', which gives a more detailed example of written instructions).

Setting the homework
Go over the instructions. Parents will be able to provide more information about driving and the rules of the road. Where this is a problem, children could be asked to choose a different subject to write about, eg a recipe.

Back at school
Go over the correct sequence of instructions for setting off and share children's instructions for the other two sections.

p61 PORTO PASO REPORT

Objective
Write a non-chronological report. (Y4, T1, T27)

Lesson context
This focuses on report writing. The background for this report can be found on page 53, 'The resort of the millenium'. This is the final activity in the series based on the imaginary city of Porto Paso. See also pages 46, 50, 53, 55–57 and 59.

Setting the homework
Explain that the report refers to the Porto Paso Development Plan on page 53, 'The resort of the millenium'. Page 53 should be given to the children along with this one. Children should imagine how the development has progressed. As long as what they write fits the basic facts on page 53, they have a completely free rein: their report can be positive or negative.

Differentiation
The less able could be given a modified page with fewer sections.

Back at school
Share the reports and discuss the differences.

TERM 2

p62 CHEFS AND CHIEFS

Objective
Investigate what happens to words ending in -f when suffixes are added. (Y4, T2, W5)

Lesson context
Use this homework as reinforcement to teaching spelling, particularly the spelling of plurals.

Setting the homework
Go over the explanation, and emphasise the importance of learning the exceptions.

Differentiation
The less able should take care to spot exceptions.

Back at school
Monitor the application of this spelling rule. Children could find other exceptions through their reading.

p63 DAMSEL IN DISTRESS

Objective
Spell words with common endings: -ight/-ite. (Y4, T2, W6)

Lesson context
This homework can be part of a study of spelling through common letter strings, or can be linked to work on rhyme (see page 34, 'Silly Billy').

Setting the homework
Explain that the two letter strings -ight and -ite have the same sound but are used in different words. There is no rule for this. Playing with rhyme is a good way to learn to spell.

Differentiation
The less able can find rhymes for the poem if the word at the end of the second line is supplied ('knight', 'alight').

Back at school
Share some of the children's poems. Monitor the use of these letter strings in day-to-day writing.

p64 GOT A NICE GARDEN

Objective
Use alternative words and expressions which are more accurate or interesting than the common choices, eg *got*, *nice*. (Y4, T2, W9)

Lesson context
This homework is good preparation for creative writing, or as part of the redrafting process.

Setting the homework
It is important to tell the children that there is nothing wrong with the words 'nice' and 'got' – they are perfectly correct English. However, they are overused.

Differentiation
The 'got' sentences are more difficult as some of them need re-phrasing. Less able could be asked to do the first three of these only.

Back at school
Share the different words that children thought of. Do the same activity with other overworked words.

p65 WHERE'S MY PARTNER?

Objective
Explore and discuss the implications of words which imply gender, including the -ess suffix. (Y4, T2, W10)

Lesson context
Follow-up to reading a text which contains examples of such words, eg a folk tale that uses the word 'shepherdess' or an article discussing 'women priests'.

Setting the homework
Explain the task, particularly the second one. Encourage children to seek the help of their helper.

Differentiation
Less able children could do the first task only.

Back at school
Quickly go over the matching exercise, then explore which feminine forms are little used today. Discuss reasons for this.

p66 WHO'S MY PARTNER?

Objective
Explore and discuss the implications of words which imply gender. (Y4, T2, W10)

Lesson context
This explores feminine forms which are created in other ways than adding the -ess suffix.

Setting the homework
Encourage children to seek help, as the activity requires wider general knowledge than many children possess. Point out that children will find fewer feminine forms that are rarely used than in the previous homework.

Differentiation
Less able children could do the first task only.

Back at school
Go over the matching exercise, then explore which feminine forms are little used today. Discuss reasons why there are far fewer than in the previous homework. (The reason is that the addition of a suffix implies some kind of modification of the basic form which in turn implies that the basic form is male. However most of the words on this list are words in their own right – except 'heroine'.)

p67 ARSELING-POLE

Objective
Understand that vocabulary changes over time. (Y4, T2, W11)

Lesson context
Use in the study of language change, or as a preparation for reading older literature – the period of change in this list is from the 18th to the mid-20th century.

Setting the homework
Explain that vocabulary changes over time because:
• many jobs and objects have disappeared
• new jobs and objects have been created
• old words are replaced by new words for the same thing
• fashionable, slang, or dialect words change frequently
Explain that the children will investigate these changes by highlighting the different kinds of words in different colours so they will need three different coloured pens or pencils.

Differentiation
The more able could work on page 68, 'Glossary', as this extends the range of words back to the 12th century.

Back at school
Collect information from the investigation. Add any words that children found out from their parents.

p68 GLOSSARY

Objective
Understand that vocabulary changes over time. (Y4, T2, W11)

Lesson context
This page is designed to be used with page 81, 'Robin and Gandelyn', but it can also be used by itself, or with page 67, 'Arseling-pole'.

Setting the homework
If using with page 81, 'Robin and Gandelyn' (a ballard written between the 12th and 16th centuries), see the notes on that page about how to set the homework. If using as a stand-alone sheet, or with page 67, delete the three tasks and the 'Dear Helper' note. Ask children to classify words by highlighting with different colours: words which died out a long time ago; words which died out recently; words which are still used occasionally today.

Differentiation
This page should be used with more able children only.

Back at school
Discuss how children classified the words. (All ME words died out a long time ago. The -eth, -st words and ye, died out more recently.

p69 ENJOYABLE, DELIGHTFUL, CHILDLIKE

Objective
Explore suffixes which can be added to nouns and verbs to make adjectives. (Y4, T2, W13)

Lesson context
Use as part of a series of lessons on spelling, or as a follow-up to reading a text with words ending with these suffixes.

Setting the homework
Revise the terms *nouns, verbs, adjectives, suffixes*. Explain the activity is to match the root word with the appropriate suffix.

Differentiation
Very weak children could be asked to do the first ten only.

Back at school
Use an OHT of the page and write in the correct words with suffixes.

p70 SHOCKING, DYNAMIC, NEWSWORTHY!

Objective
Explore suffixes which can be added to nouns and verbs to make adjectives. (Y4, T2, W13)

Lesson context
Use as part of a series of lessons on spelling, or as a follow-up to reading a text which contains several examples of words ending with these suffixes.

Setting the homework
Revise the terms *nouns, verbs, adjectives, suffixes*. Explain that the activity is to match the root word with the appropriate suffix.

Differentiation
Very weak children could be asked to do the first ten only.

Back at school
Use an OHT of the page and write in the correct words with suffixes.

p71 FUSSY WEREWOLF

Objective
Revise and extend work on adjectives. (Y4, T2, S1)

Lesson context
Use this homework to revise basic knowledge about adjectives, either as a preparation for writing, or to lay a foundation for further study of adjectives (see pages 72–74).

Setting the homework
Revise the term *adjective* using the explanation and examples on the page.

Differentiation
Abler children could do pages 72–74.

Back at school
Select some children to read out the passage with their chosen adjectives. Discuss the effectiveness of the adjectives and perhaps decide on a class version that could be displayed.

p72 HOROSCOPE ADJECTIVES

Objective
Revise and extend work on adjectives. (Y4, T2, S1)

Lesson context
Preparation for writing about characters in a story, or creating characters for a story. Note that it is 'twinned' with page 43, 'Horoscope adverbs' (Term 1). Nearly all of the adverbs on page 43 can be turned into adjectives by removing -ly.

Setting the homework
NOTE: Children who belong to certain religious groups may feel more comfortable if the list of adjectives are disassociated from the signs of the zodiac. Children should be told which aspect of the second task to focus on. If they are studying a story, they could be asked to choose three adjectives to describe each character.

Differentiation
The meanings of a few of the adjectives may need explaining to some children.

Back at school
Apply the chosen adjectives to the context of the lesson.

p73 CARRY MY CASE

Objective
Revise and extend work on adjectives: comparing adjectives. (Y4, T2, S1)

Lesson context
Use as part of a series of lessons on adjectives (see pages 71, 72 and 74), or in preparation for writing a story, poem or description in which comparisons of adjectives will be used.

Setting the homework
Go over the explanation on the page, asking children to give their own examples.

Differentiation
More able could be asked to write the degrees of comparison for some irregular adjectives, eg 'bad', 'good'.

Back at school
Use comparisons of adjectives in a creative context, eg writing a story or description.

p74 ODDLY SHAPED

Objective
Revise and extend work on adjectives: 'adjectival phrases'. (Y4, T2, S1)

Lesson context
Use as part of a series of lessons on adjectives (see page 71, 'Fussy werewolf', page 72, 'Horoscope adjectives' and page 73, 'Carry my case'), or in preparation for writing a story in which comparisons of adjectives will be used.

Setting the homework
Go over the explanation on the page. For abler children, explain the terms *phrase* and *clause* and that adjectives can appear as single words, phrases, or clauses. Explain that some of the phrases on the page will fit more than one of the sentences, so they should try to find a suitable adjectival phrase for each sentence without using any of the phrases twice.

Differentiation
Though the concept of adjectival phrase is difficult, the task on the page is fairly easy, so almost all children will benefit from attempting it.

Back at school
Briefly go over the adjectival phrases. Discuss what happens if the sentences and the phrases are swapped round. Encourage children to use adjectival phrases in their creative writing.

p75 JASON'S LIPSTICK

Objective
Use the possessive apostrophe to mark possession. (Y4, T2, S2)

Lesson context
Use to reinforce the use of the possessive apostrophe. The possessive apostrophe is difficult to teach, the main problem being that some children will use an apostrophe with every word ending in s. One way to help is to limit the use of the possessive apostrophe to people (and creatures) only. This homework focuses on the singular use only. The plural possessive apostrophe is covered later.

Setting the homework
Go over the explanation on the page. Point out that the apostrophe should be placed above a small gap just before the s.

Differentiation
This is a game which all children can enjoy and succeed at. Abler children could be introduced to the plural possessive apostrophe by including some plural cards, eg sailors/ships, girls/changing rooms.

Back at school
Monitor the use of the possessive apostrophe in writing. Be rigorous in correcting misuse of the apostrophe. One of the reasons it is badly used by older children (and adults) is that placing it before any s becomes a habit.

p76 CAT 'O NINE TAILS

Objective
Distinguish between uses of the apostrophe for contraction and possession. (Y4, T2, S2)

Lesson context
Teach separately to the possessive apostrophe but relate them by explaining that, in both cases, the apostrophe is used to show missing letters. The apostrophe for contractions should be introduced first as this is conceptually far easier.

Setting the homework
Go over the explanation and examples. Emphasise the following in order to help children to avoid common mistakes:
• the apostrophe is placed where the letter is missed out, not where the gap between the words used to be.
• the apostrophe is placed above a small gap where the missing letter used to be.

Differentiation
None needed, though the more able could research less common uses of the apostrophe with contractions, eg 'man 'o war'.

Back at school
Monitor the use of contractions in children's writing for a) correct placing of the apostrophe; and b) appropriate use, eg in informal letters and dialogue.

p77 IMAGINARY WORLDS

Objective
Understand how writers create imaginary worlds. (Y4, T2, T1)

Lesson context
Use to prepare for writing a story based on an imaginary world. It would fit well with the study of an author who has created an imaginary world such as Tolkein or Ursula le Guin.

Setting the homework
Explain to the children that the homework page is a 'toolkit' to help with the drawing of a map. They will also need a page of blank A3 paper. Drawing the map is the first step in the creation of an imaginary world. Children should note that the pictures for the map include a mix of motives and problems, eg the Elixir of Life is a drink that will make people live for ever, but the Murky Mire is a problem. Encourage children to use their imagination and add their own ideas. The map can be used for planning stories.

Differentiation
None needed at this stage, though the less able will need help when they have to turn their maps into stories and even more so when the stories have to be written down.

Back at school
Share maps and ideas for stories based on them. The next step should be a period of oral preparation in which children make up characters and stories to go with the map and take it in turns to tell them. The final stage is to write the stories.

p78 ALIEN IN THE MALL

Objective
Understand how settings influence events and incidents in stories and how they affect characters' behaviour. (Y4, T2, T2)

Lesson context
This can be used by itself but will be most effective when used with page 86, 'Alien planet'. Together, these pages can be used to explore the effects of settings on plots and characters' behaviour. The contrast between characters and settings is deliberately extreme so that all children can understand the concept.

Setting the homework
Ask children to explore the effect of characters on settings by:
• matching each character to the most appropriate setting;
• matching each character to the most unlikely setting;
• experimenting with shuffling the cards and pairing them picture side down.
Choose one or two character and setting combinations from each method of pairing, and jot down notes on the following:
• how the character would react in that setting;
• notes for a story or scene from a story.
If you do send page 86 home as well, you will need to adapt the instructions so helpers understand the task.

Differentiation
The less able could make notes about one match only from each method of pairing.

Back at school
Discuss the homework: Ask: which combinations of character and setting are silly? Which could be developed into good stories? (Example: Children - Desert Island. This combination was used very effectively in Lord of the Flies, by William Golding.)

p79 LAND OF SNOW-CAPPED MOUNTAINS

Objective
Compare and contrast settings across a range of stories. (Y4, T2, T3)

Lesson context
A follow-up to a shared reading session in which the focus was the study of settings, or as preparation for a story writing lesson.

Setting the homework
Revise the terms adjectives and figures of speech. Note that, the latter can be narrowed down to similes and metaphors. Explain the importance of 'telling details'. A fully detailed description of a scene would take pages, and would probably be very dull. Writers select a few 'telling details' to suggest a scene and the reader's imagination fills in the rest.

Differentiation
Less able children may have difficulty identifying adjectives, similes and metaphors. They could instead underline words and phrases that are 'good description'. Children of average ability should be asked to look for similes only. The more able could look for metaphors and research other examples of settings.

Back at school
Ask: What have you learned about the way writers describe settings? Encourage the children to apply the skill to the study of an author's descriptions of settings, or to writing their own settings for use in stories.

p80 SEE, SAW, STEGOSAUR

Objective
Understand the use of figurative language in poetry and prose: simile. (Y4, T2, T5)

Lesson context
This activity reinforces knowledge of the term simile and can be used for this purpose as a follow–up to a lesson on poetry or descriptive prose, or as a 'one off' for children who have not yet grasped the term.

Setting the homework
Revise the term simile, using the example in the first verse. Explain how to write about similes using the example at the bottom of the page. Saying why a simile is effective is not always easy, but it is important, because it helps children to understand what the writer is trying to say.

Differentiation
Use the first task only for simple reinforcement of the term simile. Use both tasks to teach the more difficult process of writing about similes.

Back at school
Discuss children's explanations of the similes in the poem. Apply this knowledge to the study of another poem, and write about similes along with other aspects of the poem such as subject, verse form and personal response. Ask for children's responses to the question: What is the tiny mammal in the last verse? (A human, perhaps?)

p81 ROBIN AND GANDELYN

Objective
Identify clues which suggest poems are older: eg language use, vocabulary, archaic words. (Y4, T2, T6)

Lesson context
This fine ballad can be used in several contexts: the study of ballads (several examples are provided in these books and in 100 Literacy Hours), the study of verse form (ballad form is commonly used and is easy for children to write), or the study of language change. This ballad was chosen particularly for the latter context and has not been modernised (apart from the spelling of words which are still used). This homework can also be related to page 92, 'Legend or history?'

Setting the homework
Brainstorm knowledge of Robin Hood. Explain that this is one of two versions of Robin Hood's death. This one is less well known. The task is to read the poem, highlight archaic words (explain that 'archaic' means 'no longer in common use') and try to guess their meaning from the context. The story line is clear and simple, so the archaic words should not present too great a barrier to comprehension.

Differentiation
Give less able children page 68, 'Glossary', to look up the meaning of the archaic words and for writing the meanings in the appropriate place in their ballads. More able children could go on to analyse the age of the poem. They will find that it is older than Shakespeare, though it cannot be dated more accurately than some time between 1100 and 1500.

Back at school
Discuss how many archaic words children found. The next step is to relate the homework back to the general context (see above).

p82 LOTS OF LEGS

Objective
Identify different patterns of rhyme and rhythm in poetry: *rhyming couplets*. (Y4, T2, T7)

Lesson context
This homework, along with page 80, 'See saw, Stegosaur', page 81, 'Robin and Gandelyn' (ballad form) and page 83, 'The creature of Croglin' (alternate rhyme) can be used to explore different patterns of rhyme in poetry.

Setting the homework
Revise the term *rhyme*: words ending with the same sound. Explain how to annotate rhyme schemes using letters of the alphabet, *a* for the first rhyme, *b* for the second and so on. Couplets are annotated *a a, b b* etc.

Differentiation
The task can be made easier for the less able by filling in either all the rhymes or all the riddles (names of horror creatures), so that they can concentrate on one thing.

Back at school
Go over the rhymes and the riddles and ask children to try to write similar rhyming couplets. They could add more verses to this 'Ghoulography' or they could choose another subject, eg animals, countries etc. Answers to the riddles are: alien, ghost, mummy, ogre, troll, unicorn, yeti.

p83 THE CREATURE OF CROGLIN

Objective
Identify different patterns of rhyme and rhythm in poetry: *alternate rhyme*. (Y4, T2, T7)

Lesson context
This homework, along with page 80, 'See saw, Stegosaur', page 81, 'Robin and Gandelyn' (ballad form) and page 82, 'Lots of legs' (couplets) can be used to explore different patterns of rhyme in poetry. This is also a good exercise in reading poetry aloud, as the poem contains several examples of *enjambment* (run-on lines).

Setting the homework
Revise the term *rhyme*: words ending with the same sound. Explain how to annotate rhyme schemes using letters of the alphabet, *a* for the first rhyme, *b* for the second and so on. Alternate rhymes are annotated *a b a b*, etc. Ask children to practise reading the poem aloud. Explain that they should ignore the lines, but follow the punctuation, eg not: '...eyes that seemed to creep (pause) towards her'; but '...eyes that seemed to creep towards her (pause)'.

Differentiation
Sheets for the less able could have some of the rhymes written in. The rhymes are as follows: Hall, shriek, sleep, light, door, floor, light, gun. The more able could write a continuation referred to in the second task.

Back at school
Discuss the rhymes and ideas for continuation. If any children have written continuations they could be read out.

p84 KNITTING NEEDLE DATABASE

Objective
Review a range of stories, identifying authors and themes. (Y4, T2, T8)

Lesson context
Could be linked to cross-curricular work on databases as children will be making a very simple mechanical database using punched cards. In literacy terms, the punched cards contain a format for book reviews. This is best approached as an ongoing process by which the data cards will be built up over a period of time.

Setting the homework
Prepare the basic materials. Find a suitable box (eg a shoebox), cut cards to fit the width of the box. The photocopier's magnification can be adjusted to make cards of the correct size. The important thing is that the holes or slots in the cards are aligned when they are in the box. Prepare some cards as examples. Explain how the data cards work by showing children the box and the examples. All cards about books with animals will have a HOLE above 'Animals' and SLOTS above every other category. Thus, when a knitting needle is placed through the cards, only the animal books are selected. The cards can be turned over to select by author. Note: it would be possible to sort by two other categories by using the reverse of the card, with holes at either side. If time allows, it would be better for the cards to be prepared by the teacher or an ancillary to ensure accuracy, leaving children to do the writing.

Differentiation
More able children could give a more detailed review using the reverse side of the page.

Back at school
Continue to build up the 'Knitting needle database'. Encourage children to use it to find books they are interested in and to read each others' reviews. If appropriate resources are available, the data could be transferred onto a computer database.

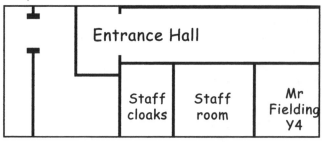

p85 SCHOOL SETTING

Objective
Develop use of settings in own writing. (Y4, T2, T10)

Lesson context
This detailed plan of a school can be used to provide a setting for a story.

Setting the homework
Discuss the plan, and point out some examples of things which could be developed into stories, eg a child falls into a pond, a ghost is seen in the Old Infant School, etc. The task is to develop a story based on the setting and to make notes for it. The children will need to invent characters, eg children, parents, teachers, caretaker, dinner ladies, lunchtime supervisors, etc. A complementary set of story cards can be found in *100 Literacy Hours: Year 4* (see pages 89–92). The plan of the setting can be used with School Cards to create a comprehensive story-telling resource.

Differentiation
The less able will need help when it comes to producing the written version of their story ideas.

Back at school
Share ideas, then follow up with the written versions of the stories. If time allows, develop oral story telling as this is a valuable preparation for writing.

p86 ALIEN PLANET

Objective
Develop use of settings in own writing. (Y4, T2, T10)

Lesson context
This set of cards can be used by itself to explore settings, or with page 78, 'Alien in the mall', to explore the effects of settings on characters.

Setting the homework
Explain that the pictures are just starting points. Go over the task. If time allows, one of the cards can be used as an example and children can fill out the details in a brainstorming session.

Differentiation
The less able could develop the card that was the subject of the brainstorming session, while others should be asked to choose a different setting.

Back at school
Share ideas for developing the settings and ask the children to develop their notes into a detailed description of a setting. Use this setting in a story. The skill here is to pick out parts of the description for use when appropriate. It is not effective to have all the description in one block.

p87 WHALE

Objective
Write poetry based on the structure and style of poems read. (Y4, T2, T11)

Lesson context
This supports children who find writing poetry very difficult. The model poem is written in free verse and has a very simple structure. It can also be used to teach the concept of lineation: the unit of the poem is the line and many children write free verse poems like prose, with no thought given to line division.

Setting the homework
Revise the terms *adjective, verb, phrase, adverb* and *simile* and explain that knowledge of these will be necessary when following the prompts in the table.

Differentiation
Less able children, and those who have difficulty understanding any of the above terms, should keep referring back to the model poem. The more able should depart from the model and develop their poem in any way they wish.

Back at school
Share the poems written and discuss ways in which they can be further developed.

p88 STONEHENGE

Objective
Edit a passage by deleting the less important elements. (Y4, T2, T14)

Lesson context
Preparing for research using non-fiction texts. All too often children simply copy the information they find. This exercise will help them to focus on the key points.

Setting the homework
Explain that, in this information text about Stonehenge, there is a 'core' of essential factual information. The rest is interesting, but not essential. The task is to pick out the essential information.

Differentiation
Give the less able children the following clue: look for sentences including the word 'imagine' or 'amazing'. These words show that the material is based on the author's idea of what it 'might' have been like, not on factual information.

Back at school
Discuss which pieces of information were factual and essential.

p89 NON-FICTION REVIEW

Objective
Appraise non-fictions books for their content. (Y4, T2, T15)

Lesson context
Use after a lesson or series of lessons involving research from non-fiction books.

Setting the homework
Ask the children to fill in the second section during the lesson to help them remember which books they used. The page would benefit from enlargement to A3 size to allow more space for writing. Alternatively, children could be asked to use both sides of the page.

Differentiation
The less able should review two books only.

Back at school
Discuss a) the qualities of a good non-fiction book; b) the process of retrieving information.

p90 ARMOUR

Objective
Mark extracts by selecting key headings, words or sentences. (Y4, T2, T18)

Lesson context
Preparing for research using non-fiction texts. This exercise focuses on picking out information on one topic which is mixed in with other topics.

Setting the homework
Explain that, when researching a topic, we often find texts where the information we are looking for is mixed in with other topics. The homework page is an example, because the information about helmets is mixed in with general information about armour. The task is to pick out the information by underlining or highlighting and then to use the information as the basis of a short article.

Differentiation
Help less able children by telling them to find the word 'helmet' and then highlight the sentence in which they found the word. They could also omit the second task.

Back at school
Discuss the information that was picked out and invite some children to read their articles. Apply the skill to a research task.

p91 FLYING MACHINES

Objective
Identify how and why paragraphs are used to organise and sequence information. (Y4, T2, T19)

Lesson context
Preparing to write non-fiction.

Setting the homework
Go over the explanation. In particular, ensure that children understand the difference between indented and blocked paragraphs. The task provides practice in layout of paragraphs, grouping information by topic, and adding subheadings.

Differentiation
Emphasise to less able children that there are four paragraphs, an introduction and a description of three different kinds of flying machine: balloon, aeroplane, rocket. The more able could add additional paragraphs of information, eg jet aircraft, jumbo jets, supersonic aircraft, etc.

Back at school
Briefly discuss how children paragraphed the text and the subheadings they chose. Then, apply the skill to writing a real piece of research in paragraphs.

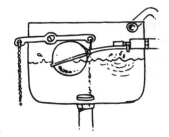

p92 LEGEND OR HISTORY?

Objective
Fill out brief notes into connected prose. (Y4, T2, T22)

Lesson context
This page provides practice for the middle stage of the research progress – turning notes into connected prose. Note that the subject provides excellent background material for page 81, 'Robin and Gandelyn'. Thus, this topic can be treated as a worthwhile research topic in its own right.

Setting the homework
Introduce or revise the term: *prose*. Prose is ordinary writing in sentences – contrast with *poetry*. Then use a brainstorming session to elicit general background information about Robin Hood. Introduce the question: *Is the story of Robin Hood a legend or is it based on history?* Explain that the task is to put the notes into sentences. The following can be given as an example: Robin Hood was an earl who was made an outlaw and went to live in Sherwood Forest. Explain that children who have extra information, or who are keen to find out, may include it, but that it is not essential. The task will be judged on how well the notes are made into connected prose.

Differentiation
The less able should write down the example given above, and use it both as a starting point and a model. The more able should add to the notes from their own knowledge and research before turning them into connected prose.

Back at school
Invite some children to read out their short articles and ask the class to evaluate each one, on the smoothness of the prose.

p93 ARENA

Objective
Collect information from a variety of sources and present it in one simple format. (Y4, T2, T23)

Lesson context
Can be used as a preparation for researching a topic from a range of books. The page simulates the different kinds of material that children will find.

Setting the homework
Explain that the homework is a simulation of real research, the main difference being that the relevant extracts have already been selected. The task is to use the information to write a brief history of the Roman Arena. There are two parts to the task. One is to pick out the essential information, the other is to place the information in an appropriate sequence.

Differentiation
The more able could find additional information. Those who do this should be given an extended word limit of 200–250 words.

Back at school
Compare different versions and discuss their relative merits. Note that the extracts themselves suggest an appropriate sequence through their time references (information from *The History of Zoos* would be used last because of the statement 'the spirit of the arena survives today'). Possible cuts include some of the details about the Colosseum, gladiatorial combats and wild beasts. Details of Perpetua's martyrdom could also be omitted. Soon after going over the task, apply the skills in a real research context.

p94 FLUSHED WITH SUCCESS

Objective
Improve the cohesion of written explanations. (Y4, T2, T24)

Lesson context
Preparing for the final draft of a non-fiction text, particularly an explanation.

Setting the homework
Explain that the text is a first draft of an explanation. The ideas have been written down quickly, but need redrafting to make them clear. Go over the task which explains clearly what must be done to turn this first draft into a clear explanation. The first few statements can be connected as an example of how to fill the gaps: *When* the handle is pulled, a lever lifts a valve *which* lets the water out of the cistern. *This* flows down a pipe and flushes the toilet.

Differentiation
This is a difficult exercise as the text has to be provided with link words and phrases, paragraphs and subheadings. The less able could be given page 90, 'Flying machines', instead, which has an easier paragraphing task and does not require the insertion of link words and phrases.

Back at school
Go over the passage and then apply the skill to redrafting the non-fiction work in progress.

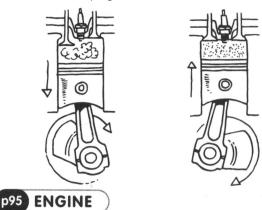

p95 ENGINE

Objective
Write explanations of a process using conventions identified through reading. (Y4, T2, T25)

Lesson context
As a follow-on from a lesson in which a similar explanatory text has been studied (see previous page). It is a complete exercise in itself, but can be used as preparation for writing explanatory texts in other areas of the curriculum.

Setting the homework
Explain the task and emphasise that the explanation must be written in sentences and paragraphs. It may contain subheadings if children wish. Refer to models that children have studied (see previous page). It would be a good idea to explain how the internal combustion engine works so that children know what they are writing about. The important thing they need to keep in mind is that the piston is always moving.

Differentiation
The more able could do some extra research so that they can add more detail to their explanations.

Back at school
Share and discuss the explanations, then apply the skill to writing about a process in another area of the curriculum.

TERM 3

p96 SS

Objective
Explore the occurrence of certain letters: ss. (Y4, T3, W5)

Lesson context
A follow-up to any text where examples of this letter string occur.

Setting the homework
Explain the task. Warn children to take extra care with the last three words. They may use a dictionary if necessary.

Back at school
Go over the exercise, then monitor the use of this letter string in children's day-to-day writing.

p97 FROM AQUA TO AQUARIUM

Objective
Collect/classify words with common roots. (Y4, T3, W7)

Lesson context
A follow-up to any text that contains a number of words based on Latin roots, or as part of a study on language history.

Setting the homework
Explain that all these root words are from Latin, which has had a great influence on the development of English. Encourage children to study the cards before cutting them up.

Differentiation
More able children could match the extra words to the roots and the very able could find other words which have come from these Latin roots.

Back at school
Check the homework as a whole-class activity. Additional Latin roots you might suggest children find modern words for are: *circum* (round) and *manus* (hand).

p98 BOY OVERBOARD

Objective
Investigate links between meaning and spelling. (Y4, T3, W8)

Lesson context
This homework can be combined with page 30, 'I see the sea', for an extended study of homophones.

Setting the homework
Explain that differences in spelling are used to show differences in meaning in many words that sound the same. This is often used to create jokes.

Differentiation
Some children may be able to describe the different meanings of the homophones to their helper, but not be able to spell them. In this case, the helper could write the word first and the child after.

Back at school
Go over the homophones, then share the humorous sentences that children made up. Monitor children's writing for confusion between words with the same sound but different spelling.

p99 POSSIBLE...AND PROBABLE!

Objective
Recognise and spell suffixes: *-ible, -able*. (Y4, T3, W9)

Lesson context
This could be set as part of a series of lessons on commonly confused endings, or it could be given as a one-off to children who make a mistake of this kind.

Setting the homework
Explain that the reason these endings are confused is that both the *i* and the *a* are pronounced as a light *uh* sound in most words. This is a perfectly correct pronunciation as many unstressed vowels are pronounced in the same way in English. The best way to learn the endings is to follow the tip on the bottom of the page.

Differentiation
Check that the less able understand all the words in the list.

Back at school
Give children a quick test on the endings and share any additional words that children thought of. Monitor the spelling of these endings in day-to-day writing.

p100 COMMOTION AND CONFUSION

Objective
Recognise and spell suffixes: *-tion, -sion*. (Y4, T3, W9)

Lesson context
Set as part of a series of lessons on commonly confused endings, or it could be given as a one-off to children who make mistakes of this kind.

Setting the homework
Explain that the reason these endings are confused is that both are pronounced 'shun'. So, the only way to learn the words is by practising them.

Differentiation
Check that the less able understand all the words in the list.

Back at school
Give children a quick test on the endings and share any additional words that children thought of. Monitor the spelling of these endings in day-to-day writing.

p101 IS IT ITS?

Objective
Distinguish between two forms: *its* and *it's*. (Y4, T3, W10)

Lesson context
Confusion of these two words is a very common mistake. Set this homework after one of the (many) occasions when a number of children have got them confused. For a very specific problem like this, it is preferable to give the homework page to individuals as needed, not to the whole class.

Setting the homework
In this homework, an additional form, 'it is', has been included. The reason for this is that 'it is' cannot be confused with 'its', and it is the form that children should use most. The shortened form should be used for dialogue and informal letters only. Go over the explanation with the children. Add the tip given in the helper's note at the bottom of the page.

Differentiation
None needed if set on an individual basis.

Back at school
Use an OHT of the homework page and invite children to write their answers in the gaps. Monitor the use of these forms in children's day-to-day writing.

p102 BABY BANK

Objective
Investigate compound words. (Y4, T3, W11)

Lesson context
Use as a follow-up to a text that contains several compound words, or as part of a study of language change.

Setting the homework
Explain to the children that a compound word is made up of two other words, eg 'skateboard', 'toothache'. Breaking compound words up into their two words will help with spelling. Encourage children to find existing compounds, and then invent new ones.

Differentiation
Knowing when a compound word should be two separate words, a hyphenated word or a single word is difficult but the less able should not worry about this.

Back at school
Discuss which existing compound words were found and which new words were made up. Have fun sharing the invented dictionary definitions. A further follow-up would be to investigate the use of the hyphen in compound words. See page 104, 'Oh dash!'

p103 BIG AND LITTLE

Objective
Understand how diminutives are formed. (Y4, T3, W12)

Lesson context
A follow-up to reading a text that contains diminutives.

Setting the homework
Go over the explanation of *diminutives* and explain the task. It is also worth pointing out that the normal form of the word is sometimes different from the diminutive – eg the normal form of 'kitten' is not 'kit', but 'cat'!

Differentiation
Some of the diminutives are not in common use, so all children, especially the less able, should be encouraged to look up words which they do not know.

Back at school
Display an OHT of the page and invite children to match the pairs. Highlight the suffixes used and ask children if they can think of any other diminutives using those suffixes.

p104 OH DASH!

Objective
Identify the common punctuation marks: *dash* and *hyphen*. (Y4, T3, S2)

Lesson context
Use as part of a study of punctuation, or in preparation for writing.

Setting the homework
Go over the explanation so that children are clear about the different uses of dashes and hyphens and the different ways they are written.

Differentiation
Children who have not mastered the use of the full stop, question mark, exclamation mark and commas in lists should do more work on these before moving on to dashes and hyphens.

Back at school
Encourage children to a) use dashes expressively in their writing, and b) remember to hyphenate compound words where necessary, particularly numbers.

p105 MANDY'S STUDIO

Objective
Identify the common punctuation marks: *comma, semi-colon, colon*. (Y4, T3, S2)

Lesson context
Use as part of a study of punctuation or as a preparation for descriptive writing.

Setting the homework
Go over the explanation emphasising that these three punctuation marks are often used together to punctuate complex lists. Draw children's attention to the pattern.

Differentiation
Children who cannot write simple lists using commas and 'and' should write three separate sentences with simple lists to describe each area of the studio. More able children could experiment by writing the items in a different order, then choose the one that sounds best.

Back at school
Ask volunteers to write their lists on the board and others to comment on how accurately they have been punctuated.

p106 TURN IT DOWN!

Objective
Understand how the grammar of a sentence alters when the sentence type is altered. (Y4, T3, S4)

Lesson context
Use as part of a series of lessons on sentences, or as a follow-up to reading a text which contains the four sentence types.

Setting the homework
Go over the four different types of sentences. Emphasise that questions must alway end with a question mark. The use of exclamation marks often depends on how something is said or written. If a sentence is meant to convey excitement or urgency, it should end with an exclamation mark.

Differentiation
The less able should focus on the use of the question and exclamation mark. The more able could analyse the different types of sentence by looking for patterns in the order of subject (S), verb (V) and object (O).

Back at school
Ask children to identify the four types of sentence in a book they are reading.

p107 ONLY CONNECT

Objective
Investigate the use of connectives to structure an argument. (Y4, T3, S4)

Lesson context
Use as a preparation for argumentative writing. This page can be used by itself, or with page 125, 'Five-point plan'. Page 120, 'Skyliner complaint' and page 121, 'Unsafe at any speed' might also be used as part of a series on investigating connectives.

Setting the homework
This homework is mainly oral. Give children a topic to discuss, eg, School Uniform, Fox Hunting, Recycling. They should read through the list of connectives and discuss the topic with their helper. They should jot down any other connectives which arise in discussion. Finally, they could make notes in preparation for writing on the topic.

Back at school
Make an OHT of the page and add to it all the additional connectives. Re-run the discussion, continuing to add to the list as new connectives arise. Finally, ask the children to copy all the connectives they do not have, thus making a valuable resource to support their own writing.

p108 BINA'S BETROTHAL

Objective
Identify social, moral or cultural issues in a story. (Y4, T3, T1)

Lesson context
Any shared or guided reading session where a text that raises issues has been discussed, particularly one where conflicts of culture are an issue.

Setting the homework
This extract raises the issues of arranged marriages. It is worth pointing out to all children, whatever their cultural background, that most societies have practised arranged marriages at some time in their history (eg it was common in England until the nineteenth century). Also, it is worth challenging the assumption that marrying for love is always preferable to an arranged marriage – witness the high divorce rate in Western European society today when people choose their mates. The issue should be discussed in the context of the story. Bina stands to lose a great deal if she goes against her community. Is it worth it? Explain that the purpose of the discussion is to provide ideas for the next episode in the story.

Differentiation
More able children could be asked to carry out the extension activity.

Back at school
Ask children who have undertaken the extension activity to share their next episodes. Discuss the issues raised in these episodes. The story could be further developed so that it has a conclusion which shows the wisdom or otherwise of Bina's choice.

p109 BANJA'S COMING OF AGE

Objective
Read stories from other cultures by focusing on: customs. (Y4, T3, T2)

Lesson context
Use in the context of reading stories from other cultures as a focus for examining similarities and differences.

Setting the homework
After reading the story, ask children to discuss the questions at the top of the page with their helper. This will help them develop empathy with the Kung people, and in particular, with Banja, a young person 'coming of age' in his society. The continuation should be another episode in Banja's trial – not necessarily the whole story to the end.

Differentiation
More able children could be asked to carry out the extension activity.

Back at school
Discuss the questions at the top of the page. Ask children who have undertaken the extension activity to share some of the continuations and discuss how well they fit what we already know of Banja and his environment.

p110 THE DEATH OF ROBIN HOOD

Objective
Understand the following terms and identify them in poems: *verse*, *chorus*, *couplet*, *stanza*, *rhyme*, *rhythm*, *alliteration*. (Y4, T3, T4)

Lesson context
This could be used as revision and consolidation of the terms on the page. It could also be part of a study of poetic techniques along with pages 111–114; or part of a study of ballads, along with page 81, 'Robin and Gandelyn'. Note that these two ballads give alternative versions of Robin Hood's death. The version in this ballad is generally the accepted version.

Setting the homework
Add the following information: A long verse (often with an irregular pattern of rhyme) is usually called a *stanza*. The term *chorus* is usually applied to songs (or song-like poems) while the term *refrain* is more often used for poetry.

Differentiation
There are a lot of terms for the less able to take in. Give them two or three to concentrate on as appropriate.

Back at school
Display an OHT of the poem and invite children to identify the features. This work could be consolidated by asking children to find examples of the terms in other poems.

p111 HAIKU

Objective
Clap out and count syllables in poetry. (Y4, T3, T5)

Lesson context
Use as part of a study of poetic techniques along with pages 110, 112–114, and/or reading and writing haiku.

Setting the homework
Reading and writing *haiku* is a very good way to get into syllable counting as the haiku form depends entirely on syllables, not on rhythm or rhyme. Explain that the homework is a simulation of the skills required to write haiku – count syllables, and express an idea in a set number of syllables.

Differentiation
The less able could practise counting syllables before doing the homework. The more able could write haiku of their own.

Back at school
Go over the syllable count for each line and discuss ways of correcting lines that are too long or too short. Follow up immediately with reading some more examples of haiku and by children writing their own.

p112 LUCKY DOG!

Objective
Clap out and count syllables and stresses in each regular rhyme of poetry. (Y4, T3, T5)

Lesson context
Use as part of a study of poetic techniques along with pages 110–111, 113–114; and/or as a preparation for studying a poem written in traditional rhyming verse.

Setting the homework
The aim is to explain the basis of rhythm in English poetry. Go over the explanation and relate it to the example. Explain to children that the best way to hear syllables or stress is to read the verses aloud in a strong voice and to beat time.

Differentiation
Less able children may confuse syllables and stress and should be given individual work to practise these. The more able could be given some additional verses to analyse.

Back at school
Go over the children's answers, then apply the skills to the study of a longer poem.

p113 OLD LADY FROM CHINA

Objective
Describe how a poet uses rhyme. (Y4, T3, T6)

Lesson context
Use as part of a study of poetic techniques along with pages 110–112 and 114. This is also part of learning to write about a poem. Writing about a poem should include some or all of the following: discussion of the poet's message; explanation of how the message is expressed, eg verse form, figurative language and vocabulary; a personal response to the poem.

Setting the homework
Go over the explanation. Explain how important it is to try to say something about the effect of the way a poet uses rhymes, while also admitting that this is not always easy! Encourage them to 'have a go', emphasising that there are no right and wrong answers.

Differentiation
The more able could be given a poem with a more complex rhyme scheme to write about.

Back at school
Go over children's answers and, as soon as possible, apply the skill in the broader context of studying all the aspects of a poem (see above).

p114 DRACULA?

Objective
Describe how a poet does or does not use rhyme. (Y4, T3, T6)

Lesson context
Use as part of a study of poetic techniques along with pages 110–113, and/or as a preparation for reading or writing free verse poems.

Setting the homework
Free verse is frequently set out like prose – indeed it often is prose because it is written in sentences! This exercise makes the children focus closely on line breaks – which is one of the main techniques in free verse. Review the definition of 'free verse' and, if there is time, read the poem aloud.

Differentiation
It is much easier to get the idea about line breaks than it is to explain it. Therefore, the less able could be asked to show their understanding by writing a free verse poem which is set out in a similar way to 'Dracula?' – eg with short lines.

Back at school
Discuss the reasons for the poet's line breaks, and share examples of poems that children have written. Apply the knowledge to the study of a free-verse poem.

p115 MNEMONIC RHYMES

Objective
Recognise some simple forms of poetry: menomonic rhymes. (Y4, T3, T7)

Lesson context
This can be used as one of a series of lessons exploring different kinds of verse.

Setting the homework
Encourage children to find other examples of mnemonic rhymes, in particular by asking parents, grandparents and other adults. They could also be set specific items to write mnemonics for – this will depend on topics currently being studied, but history and geography usually provide good examples.

Back at school
Ask selected children to recite their chosen poems by heart. Share any other mnemonic rhymes collected or written by the children.

p116 DEATH BY WATER

Objective
Write critically about an issue or a dilemma raised in a story, explaining the problem, alternative courses of action etc. (Y4, T3, T8)

Lesson context
This activity is a good preparation for studying a longer text in which an issue is being expressed. Note that this homework is building up skills which children will need later to write literary essays. Such essays will include discussion of plot, character, themes and language.

Setting the homework
Begin by giving some background information. The extract is from a story about the famous fortune teller Michele de Notredame (known as Nostradamus) who lived from 1503–66. Nostradamus is said to have predicted many historical events including the World Wars. Encourage children to discuss the questions at the top of the page with their helper before doing the written task.

Differentiation
The more able could discuss the issue of fate in a short essay. The less able could be asked to show their understanding of the issue by planning a continuation to the story which shows whether it is possible to tell the future, or sensible to believe fortune-tellers. Alternatively, they could do page 117, 'Lost wallet', instead in which the issue for discussion is less abstract.

Back at school
Share some of the essays and continuations and discuss further the issues raised.

p117 LOST WALLET

Objective
Write critically about an issue or a dilemma raised in a story, explaining the problem, alternative courses of action etc. (Y4, T3, T8)

Lesson context
This is similar to page 116, 'Death by water', except that the issue it raises is less abstract. It can, therefore, be used at the same time as page 116 for less able children, or as a preparation for page 116.

Setting the homework
Encourage children to discuss the questions at the top of the page with their helper before doing the written task.

Differentiation
More able children could do page 116, 'Death by water', as an alternative as this raises a more abstract issue for discussion, and the written tasks are more demanding.

Back at school
Share some of the plans for story endings and discuss further the issues raised.

100 LITERACY HOMEWORK ACTIVITIES • YEAR 4 TERM 3

p118/119 ARE YOU A BOOKWORM?

Objective
Describe and review own reading habits. (Y4, T3, T10)

Lesson context
This would be a valuable homework to set mid-term as this gives an opportunity to review reading habits so far and allows time for development.

Setting the homework
This is a light-hearted quiz – with a serious purpose. Direct the children to the second task as they may wish to make notes about titles and authors of any books they have read in school.

Back at school
Page 119 provides an analysis of reader types for children to check their answers. It could be posted on the noticeboard, or circulated, one per table so that children can find out what kind of reader they are. A good follow-up to this would be to discuss the quiz in individual reading sessions so that personal recommendations and support can be given.

p120 SKYLINER COMPLAINT

Objective
Read and evaluate examples of arguments. (Y4, T3, T16)

Lesson context
This homework should be used with page 122, 'Skyliner,' as it is a complaint arising from the advertisement. Use both in the context of developing persuasive writing.

Setting the homework
Review the *Skyliner* advertisement on page 122. Tell the children that the homework involves evaluating a letter of complaint from a customer who has just returned from a holiday on *Skyliner*. Explain that they will need both the advertisement and the letter to carry out the activity. Remind them to look carefully at the small print in the advertisement.

Differentiation
Less able children could focus on the first and third tasks only.

Back at school
Discuss whether the complaints are fair. Share some of the replies. (Many of the complaints are justified because of the small print that restricted some of the service to first class only. However, it is probably unfair to complain about a crowded observation deck as everybody would want to see New York. Also, it is reasonable to expect to pay more for food prepared and served in the sky). Follow up by asking children to write letters of complaint in another context.

p121 UNSAFE AT ANY SPEED

Objective
Examine how arguments are presented. (Y4, T3, T17)

Lesson context
This page can be used by itself, or as an exemplar of how to use connectives (see page 107, 'Only connect', or see page 125, 'Five-point plan').

Setting the homework
Go over the tasks at the top of the page. If using this page with page 125, ask children to note how each paragraph fits the five-point plan. If using the page with page 107, ask children to compare the connectives with those listed.

Differentiation
Less able could focus on the first and second tasks only.

Back at school
Discuss what children have learned from studying this argumentative article and apply this knowledge to the writing of an argumentative article on another topic.

p122 SKYLINER

Objective
Evaluate advertisements for their impact, appeal and honesty. (Y4, T3, T19)

Lesson context
This page can be used by itself or as part of a series of pages (120, 121, 123, 124, 126) about the imaginary *Skyliner*. Together, these pages set up an imaginary situation which can be used as a stimulus for a range of writing.

Setting the homework
Ask children to read the advertisement carefully. When highlighting things that are persuasive, they should think about the features which they would find most attractive, eg the glass-bottomed swimming pool. To do the second task, they need to look very carefully at the advertisement as a whole (but don't mention the small print at this stage).

Back at school
Discuss the advertisement. Use the tasks at the top of the page as a focus for discussion. Broaden the discussion to include real advertisements. Follow up the study of real advertisements by asking children to design their own.

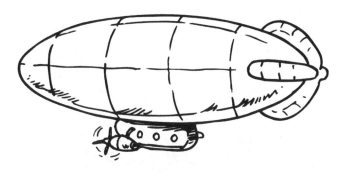

p123 SKYLINER POSTCARD

Objective
Summarise a text by identifying the most important elements. (Y4, T3, T20)

Lesson context
This page can be used by itself or as part of a series (120, 121, 122, 124, 126) about the imaginary *Skyliner*. Summarising is a key research skill. This page along with pages 124, 126 and 127 are designed to develop different aspects of the skill of summary. This is a good exercise to start with because of its informal nature.

Setting the homework
Explain that, as this is an informal letter and the postcard summary will be even more informal, children do not need to worry about producing an exact summary with all the key points. The best way to do the summary is to read the letter, then write the postcard from memory.

Differentiation
Abler children could do page 124, 'R101', instead. This is also a 50-word summary, but in this case, it is essential that all the key points are picked out.

Back at school
Share the postcard summaries. Follow up by moving on to a more challenging type of summary within a few weeks.

p124 R101

Objective
Summarise a text by identifying the most important elements. (Y4, T3, T20)

Lesson context
This is good practice for the kind of summary that children will need in real life – summarising information from a non-fiction text. This would, therefore, be good preparation for a research task. (Note that this page can be used to provide background material for the imaginery *Skyliner* simulation, the series of pages on 120, 121, 122, 123, and 126).

Setting the homework
Emphasise the second sentence of the task. This may help the children to ignore the information about Eileen Garrett. However interesting this may be, it is not factual information about the airship itself.

Differentiation
The less able could be given the tip that they should ignore all the information about Eileen Garrett.

Back at school
Compare and discuss children's summaries, then apply the skill to a real research task.

p125 FIVE-POINT PLAN

Objective
Assemble and sequence points in order to plan the presentation of a point of view. (Y4, T3, T21)

Lesson context
Use this activity after preparatory research and discussion about an issue. Note that it can be used by itself, or with page 107, 'Only connect'. This enables children to find suitable connectives for each section of their essay. Note that page 121, 'Unsafe at any speed' can be used as an example of essay structure, as it is based on the five-point plan.

Setting the homework
Enlarge the pages to A3 size to provide more room for writing, or ask children to write on separate sheets of paper. All the preparatory research and discussion about the topic will need to have been done so that children have a point of view to express and arguments to back it up.

Differentiation
The less able could write directly on the sheet, as this will support them in structuring their writing. The more able should write on paper and could be encouraged to add more paragraphs, eg they could add and develop a third point.

Back at school
Ask volunteers to read out what they have written and discuss them further both in terms of the points made, and the way the writing is structured.

p126 AVIATION BIOGRAPHIES

Objective
Summarise in writing the key ideas from a chapter: biography. (Y4, T3, T24)

Lesson context
This page along with pages 123, 124 and 127 are designed to develop different aspects of the skill of summary. Children will often need to summarise biographies as part of their research in subjects across the curriculum and this homework would be a valuable preparation.

Setting the homework
Emphasise to children that this is a fictional biography. Sir Charles Cartwright does not exist. He is the imaginary character who designed the imaginary *Skyliner* airship. Thus, this text, as well as providing an example of biography at one level, also exemplifies how non-fictional forms can be used to write fiction. The summary task is slightly more difficult than page 124, 'R101', because the less relevant material is not so obvious.

Differentiation
Pages 123, 124 and this page are of increasing difficulty. One method of differentiation would be to set them at the same time, but give them to different children as appropriate.

Back at school
Share and discuss the summaries.

p127 THE PHANTOM OF THE OPERA

Objective
Summarise in writing the key ideas from a chapter: *abridgement* of classic fiction. (Y4, T3, T24)

Lesson context
This homework focuses on a special kind of summary called *abridgement*. It can be set as one of a series of lessons on summary (see pages 123, 124 and 126), or can be linked with the reading of an abridged classic.

Setting the homework
Explain the term *abridgement*. Draw attention to the tip at the top of the page. All the descriptions in the passage can be shortened – the skill is to shorten them while still keeping the essence of the description.

Differentiation
The language and style is difficult (even though it has already been adapted). Therefore, it would be better to give the less able a simpler form of summary (see pages 123 and 124).

Back at school
Share and discuss the abridgements made by the children. An interesting follow-up would be to compare a page of an abridged classic with the original version.

Long vowels

The grid below shows the most common ways in which **long vowels** are spelled.

● Look at the examples, then add your own in the third column.

a (ay)	Examples	Your examples
a	able	
ai	pain	
ay	day	
ey	prey	
e (ee)		
e	be	
ea	plea	
ee	see	
ei	ceiling	
ie	believe	
i (eye)		
i	idle	
ie	lie	
igh	high	
uy	guy	
y	spy	
o (oh)		
o	volcano	
oa	cocoa	
oe	foe	
ough	dough	
ow	blow	
u (you)		
ew	chew	
oo	too	
ugh	through	
ue	blue	

Dear Helper,

Objective: to identify the long vowel sound in words and to see how the same sound may have different spellings.

If necessary, remind your child that the vowels are *a, e, i, o, u* (and sometimes *y*). The long sound is the name of the letter.

Hoping and hopping

Double consonants are used:

- to make the vowel before them short.
    coma because **o** is long but **comma** because **o** is short
    hoping because **o** is long but **hopping** because **o** is short

- when adding a suffix to words which end in a single vowel followed by a single consonant.
    shopping/shopped because 'shop' ends in a single vowel **o** followed by a single consonant **p**, but **failing/failed** because 'fail' has two vowels before the final consonant.

- Complete the gaps in this table.

Long vowel, single consonant	Short vowel, double consonant
coma	comma
	dinner
	bitter
taping	
	supper
wining	

- Now complete this table.

Word	Suffix	New word
hit	er	hitter
beg	ing	
big	est	
feel	ing	
yell	ing	
wait	ed	
beam	ing	
shop	er	

Dear Helper,

Objective: to spell two-syllable words containing double consonants.

Remind your child that the vowels are a, e, i, o, u (and sometimes y) and the consonants are all the other letters of the alphabet. It is often difficult to know when to use double consonants. Learning the two rules above will help. Read the explanation with your child and help them to apply it to filling in the tables.

Name:

Double trouble

- Read this poem carefully.
- Write out the rules it explains in simple prose, in the box below.

Oh, it's wining and dining and staring and sparing,
But winning and dinning and starring and sparring.
It's just one for the long 'un, but two for the short 'un,
But for longer than one sound the rule needs some sortin':

It's two in referring, preferring, deterring –
The stress at the end is what keeps occurring;
While in offering, proffering, galloped and walloped
The last letter's single, 'cept in kidnapped and worshipped,
For these two, like handicapped, have double 'p'
(There's no logic in these, so learn 'em, all three).

A second 'l' follows when adding to 'l',
Be it quarrel, or travel, or cancel, or revel.
Parallel (or unparalleled)'s the only bar to this jingle –
With two 'l's before it, the last 'l' stays single.

Rules

Dear Helper,

Objective: to learn to spell words containing double consonants.
Help your child to pick out the spelling rules from this poem and to set it out in simple prose. Encourage them to learn the rules.

I see the sea

Homophones are words which sound the same but have different meanings and spellings: *homo* (same) + *phone* (sound). They are the cause of many mistakes!

see (to look)   **allowed** (to have permission)
sea (body of water)   **aloud** (noisily)

Sometimes, there are three alternative meanings:
there (a place)   **their** (belonging to them)   **they're** (short for 'they are)'

● Circle the correct homophone from the words in brackets. If in doubt, check in a dictionary.

She looked for (there, their, they're) coats.

We went to (buy, by) some sweets.

It is (to, too, two) hot.

She (through, threw) the ball.

It went (through, threw) the window.

She settled down to (right, write) the letter.

I (hear, here) the noise.

We hoped the (weather, whether) would change.

She told a good (tail, tale).

She began the letter, '(Dear, Deer) Sir'.

Extension

● There are 5 mistakes in the paragraph below. Find them and re-write the paragraph correctly in the box.

Jake past the ball to Stella, but she missed it. Anwar caught it and through it to Handa. Unfortunately, it went write passed her into the neighbour's garden, braking the window.

Dear Helper,

Objective: to learn the spelling and meaning of words that sound the same but are spelled differently.
It is worth pointing out that homophones have a valuable purpose: the different spellings help to avoid confusion about meaning. However, there's no easy rule for spelling. The words just have to be learned!

Tense tables

Regular verbs are verbs that have endings added to the root word to change the tense.

● Complete this table.

Verb	Present tense (3rd person)	Past tense (3rd person)	Present participle (3rd person)
walk	he walk<u>s</u>	he walk<u>ed</u>	he is walk<u>ing</u>
laugh			
paint			
tremble			

● Explain what you did to the verb *tremble* before adding *-ed* and *-ing*.

Irregular verbs are verbs that have a different form in the past tense.

● Complete this table.

Verb	Present tense (3rd person)	Past tense (3rd person)	Present participle (3rd person)
tell	she tells	she told	she is telling
know			
fight			
run			
catch			

● Explain what you did to the verb *run* before adding *-ing*.
● How did you form the present tense of the verb *catch*?

Dear Helper,

Objective: to learn to spell regular and irregular verb tense endings.

Do not worry if your child finds the terminology difficult. This will come in time. Help them to complete the tables by using the words in sentences and saying them aloud. Discuss with your child spellings that require -es rather just -s (catches) and dropping the final silent e or doubling of final consonants when adding -ing (trembling, running).

PHOTOCOPIABLE

Abstract nouns

An **abstract noun** names a concept or idea rather than a specific thing:

Examples: **jealousy, love, motherhood**

The suffixes -**ship**, -**hood** and -**ness** can be added to certain nouns and adjectives to make them abstract nouns:

Examples: **father** + hood = **fatherhood**   **author** + ship = **authorship**

cold + ness = coldness

The suffixes can be added to most words without changing the spelling, but note that, words ending in **y** change the **y** to **i** before adding a suffix:

Example: **lazy** + ness = **laziness**

● Add the appropriate suffix (-**ship**, -**hood** or -**ness**) to the following nouns or adjectives to make abstract nouns. The first one has been done for you.

Noun or adjective	Abstract noun
author	authorship
awkward	
bitter	
blind	
bright	
busy	
cheerful	
child	
citizen	
false	
friend	
happy	
hard	
knight	
leader	
likely	
man	
relation	
woman	

Dear Helper,

Objective: to make abstract nouns using the suffixes: *-ship, -hood, -ness.*

Read through the list of words with your child. They should be able to choose the correct suffix through association, but help may be needed with some words.

100 LITERACY HOMEWORK ACTIVITIES • YEAR 4 TERM 1

Phantom pharoahs

- Put the words from column 1 in alphabetical order in column 2 (the first two have been done as an example).
- Give a simple definition in your own words in column 3.

Word	Arranged alphabetically	Simple definition
pie	phantom	A ghost
pheasant	pharaoh	The name for the ruler of Ancient Egypt
picture		
photograph		
pizza		
phoenix		
pig		
pharaoh		
pillar		
pile		
phobia		
phantom		
pigment		
pigeon		
phone		
picnic		
phrase		
piano		
physics		

Dear Helper,

Objectives: to use second, third and fourth letters for alphabetical ordering and to define familiar vocabulary in own words.

Your child can be helped with the first task by having a copy of the alphabet to which they can refer. For the second task, they may need help with the more difficult words. They may refer to a dictionary, but should be encouraged to re-state the definition in their own words.

Silly Billy

- Look at these three extracts from a rhyming dictionary.

-a, -ay, -eigh, -et, -ey
a, aye, bay, clay, day, fray,
grey, jay, lay, may, May, nay,
neigh, pay, play, pray, prey, ray,
Ray, say, slay, sleigh, spray,
stay, stray, sway, they, way,
weigh, array, astray, away, beret,
betray, Bombay, bouquet, cafe,
Calais, convey, decay, delay,
dismay, display, doomsday, essay,
hooray, mislay, obey, portray,
repay, subway, waylay, castaway,
Chevrolet, disobey, holiday,
yesterday.

-e, -ea, -ee, -ey, -y
be, bee, fee, flea, flee, free,
glee, he, key, knee, me, pea,
plea, quay, sea, see, she, ski,
spree, tea, three, tree, we,
agree, banshee, debris, squeegee,
bumblebee, chimpanzee, guarantee,
harmony, honey bee, pedigree,
Pharisee, referee, refugee,
symphony, tyranny, apostrophe,
catastrophe.

-i, -ie, -igh, -y, -ye
I, by, cry, dry, dye, fly, guy,
lie, my, pie, rye, sigh, tie, why.

- Find suitable words to complete the second and last verses of this ballad.

Silly Billy

Now, here's the tale of Billy boy,
A tale we all should heed,
For Billy acted without thought.
He's a silly boy, indeed.

Now, Billy was a silly boy,
He wanted to be _____,
So instead of going to school one day
He ran away to _____.

Now, Billy was a silly boy,
He wanted to get _____,
And now, instead of stuck at school
He's stuck as a _____.

- Add some middle verses to the ballad or write your own rhyming poem. You can use the back of the page.

Dear Helper,

Objective: to use a rhyming dictionary.
Spend some time helping your child to study the rhyming words. Look for homophones (words with the same sound but different spelling) and unusual words (eg 'doomsday'). Help your child to write a rhyming poem.

Verbalise it!

- Draw lines to show which **nouns** and **adjectives** have been changed into which **verbs**. The first one has been done as an example.

Nouns and adjectives	Verbs
bath	widen
circle	sharpen
cloth	moisturise
dark	obey
do	prove
drama	simplify
food	shorten
friend	grieve
frost	solidify
full	horrify
gold	freeze
grief	fill
horror	darken
life	strengthen
moisture	terrify
obedience	bathe
proof	do
sharp	befriend
short	live
simple	gild
solid	encircle
strong	clothe
terror	dramatise
wide	feed

- Can you see any patterns in the ways in which nouns and adjectives are made into verbs? Write them on the back of the page.

Dear Helper,

Objective: to investigate the ways in which nouns and adjectives can be made into verbs.
Matching words is fairly easy. Your child will need most help when it comes to looking for patterns, eg the addition of -*ify*.

Present tense

Verb tenses show the time when actions take place – in the present, past or future.

The **simple present tense** is formed from the infinitive (name) of the verb except in the third-person singular, where the infinitive + **s** is used. The simple present tense describes what is happening now, or what is done habitually.

The **present continuous tense** is formed from the verb **to be** + present participle (the **-ing** form of the verb). It describes continuous, ongoing action now.

To walk – simple present tense

	Singular	Plural
First person	I walk	we walk
Second person	you walk	you walk
Third person	he/she/it walks	they walk

To walk – present continuous tense

	Singular	Plural
First person	I am walking	we are walking
Second person	you are walking	you are walking
Third person	he/she/it is walking	they are walking

● Write verb tables like the ones above for the following verbs. Use the back of this page.

Regular
laugh
gallop
paint
tremble

Irregular
swim
sing
drive
run

Dear Helper,

Objective: to investigate the present tense of verbs.

Understanding how verb tenses are formed will help your child to write accurately and consistently. Ensure that your child reads the explanation and examples carefully and that they understand them. Help them to write verb tables – take care with *irregular verbs*!

S

Past tense

Verb tenses show the time when actions take place – in the present, past or future.

The **simple past tense** is formed from the infinitive (name) of the verb + **ed**. The simple past tense describes an action completed in the past.

The **past continuous tense** is formed from the past tense of the verb **to be** + present participle (the **-ing** form of the verb). It describes past action which took place over a period of time.

To walk – simple past tense

	Singular	Plural
First person	I walked	we walked
Second person	you walked	you walked
Third person	he/she/it walked	they walked

To walk – past continuous tense

	Singular	Plural
First person	I was walking	we were walking
Second person	you were walking	you were walking
Third person	he/she/it was walking	they were walking

- Write verb tables like the ones above for the following verbs. Use the back of this page.

Regular	**Irregular**
laugh	swim
gallop	sing
paint	drive
tremble	run

Dear Helper,

Objective: to investigate the past tense of verbs.

Understanding how verb tenses are formed will help your child to write accurately and consistently. Ensure that your child reads the explanation and examples carefully and that they understand them. Help them to write verb tables – take care with irregular verbs!

PHOTOCOPIABLE

Name:

Future tense

Verb tenses show the time when actions take place – in the present, past or future.

The **future tense** is formed with the auxiliary verb **will** + infinitive (name) of the verb. The future tense describes an action that will take place in the future.

The **future continuous tense** is formed from the future tense of the verb **to be** + present participle (the **-ing** form of the verb). It describes future action over a period of time.

To walk – future tense

	Singular	Plural
First person	I will walk	we will walk
Second person	you will walk	you will walk
Third person	he/she/it will walk	they will walk

To walk – future continuous tense

	Singular	Plural
First person	I will be walking	we will be walking
Second person	you will be walking	you will be walking
Third person	he/she/it will be walking	they will be walking

● Write verb tables like the ones above for the following verbs. Use the back of this page.

Regular	**Irregular**
laugh	swim
gallop	sing
paint	drive
tremble	run

Dear Helper,

Objective: to investigate the future tense of verbs.

Understanding how verb tenses are formed will help your child to write accurately and consistently. Ensure that your child reads the explanation and examples carefully and that they understand them. Help them to write verb tables – take care with irregular verbs!

Be kind, please rewind

The **imperative mood** of the verb is easy to recognise because the subject is not stated.

> Example: **Shut** the door!

The **imperative mood** is used for commands and instructions. It often appears at the beginning of the sentence as above, although it can appear elsewhere.

> Example: When you have finished reading, **answer** the questions.

● Find and underline the **imperative verbs** in these sentences (some sentences contain more than one).

Be quiet!

Come in.

Help me to carry these packages.

Stop talking and start working!

Put the video cassette in the slot and press play.

Be kind, please rewind.

Before we all get wet, close that window.

When you see the red light, stop.

For your safety, please keep your hands inside the vehicle.

Do not walk on the grass.

Dear Helper,

Objective: to revise work on verbs: *imperative mood.*
Help your child to find the imperative verbs by asking the questions: *What are you being asked to do? What action must you take?*

Name:

Budgie's big day

- Underline the verbs in the sentences in these five passages, using a different coloured pen for the **past**, **present** and **future** tense and the **imperative** mood.
- Say what type of writing each text is and which tense or tenses it uses.

Dear diary
I am feeling really tired this morning. Every muscle in my body is aching! I don't think I'm cut out for rock climbing! Still, I got to the top, and that was a real achievement considering I've never climbed anything higher than our stairs before! Tomorrow I'll get to the top!

Type of text _____

Tenses used _____

Magic toothbrush
Your magic toothbrush will last a lifetime if you: clean and dry it after use, replace it in its stand, keep it out of direct sunlight, and change the batteries as soon as they are flat.

Type of text _____

Tenses used _____

Why you should be a vegetarian
Every day, thousands of animals are slaughtered so that we can eat them. What is worse, in these days of factory farming, they often lead unhappy lives. They are kept in cramped conditions and force fed. All this is not necessary. It is perfectly possible, with the help of modern science, to live entirely on non-animal products. What's more – it's much healthier!

Type of text _____

Tenses used _____

Parachute
A parachute is an umbrella or wing-shaped canopy used to slow down the descent of a person, or supplies, dropped from a plane. The first parachute jump was made from a balloon by Garnerin in 1797.

Type of text _____

Tenses used _____

Budgie's big day
Budgie woke up. The clock on Granny's mantlepiece showed 8:30am. He had a drink of water, looked in his mirror, fluttered from perch to perch, and rocked vigorously on his swing. Then he looked at the clock again: 8:40. Oh, no! 8:40 and he'd done everything there was to do in his little cage – it was going to be another boring day!

Type of text _____

Tenses used _____

Dear Helper,

Objective: to investigate verb tenses by comparing sentences from narrative and information texts.

Different tenses are commonly used in different types of writing. For example, stories are often written in the past tense, while weather reports are generally in the future tense. There are, however, always exceptions and some pieces of writing will contain more than one tense! Share the reading of these texts with your child. Help them to pick out the verbs and identify tenses and text types.

Crocodile river

- Fill the gaps in the passage below with the most powerful verb you can think of. For example, in the first gap, **feared** would be more powerful than **knew**.

In this extract from Nigerian Noon, *Sulu must pass a test of courage so that he can become a warrior. The test is to swim across a river full of crocodiles.*

The river was wide and brown after the rains. Sulu could see no crocodiles, but he _____ they were there. He _____ down the river bank and began to swim. He _____ his feet as hard as he could and _____ with his arms, but he hardly seemed to move. In his mind he _____ crocodiles _____ towards him. He wanted to scream and _____. He wanted to _____, but he knew that he would fail the test and be _____ back to his mother instead of the warrior's kraal* with the other men.

   Then he _____ a long grey shape in the river. It _____ towards him at great speed. He took a deep breath and _____ to the bottom of the river where he stayed until his lungs felt like they would _____. When he surfaced, the grey shape had _____.

   Sulu _____ on until the other bank seemed nearer. He was now so exhausted that he hardly cared if a crocodile _____ him or not. At last he reached the bank and was helped out by a band of young warriors. They clapped their hands and _____ . 'You are now a man and a warrior!' they _____ . 'Come with us to our kraal'.

* kraal: a large hut woven from dried reeds

Sulu finds out later that there are no crocodiles in that part of the river. Swimming across, believing the river to be full of crocodiles, was the test of courage. The 'grey shape' was a log.

Quickly

An **adverb** describes a verb. Many adverbs are made by adding **-ly** to adjectives. In the sentence 'She ran quickly', the adverb **quickly** tells us how she ran.

- Add a different adverb to each of the following sentences:

Mr James ran _____.

He drove _____.

It rained _____.

The car stopped _____.

She laughed _____.

Jim answered _____.

The music played _____.

The girl sighed _____.

Jake did his homework _____.

Time passed _____.

- Underline the adverbs in *Escape*.

Tip: look for words ending in **-ly**.

ESCAPE

He ran quickly down the street. He looked anxiously left and right. Fortunately everything was quiet. He felt tired and rather unhappy to be running away so soon. He reached the crossroads and stopped momentarily. He started again and turned cautiously into the High Street. Suddenly he stopped. There was the sound of footsteps behind him. His heart beat violently. He was being followed!

Dear Helper,

Objective: to identify common adverbs with *-ly* endings.
Go over the explanation with your child. Help them to think of suitable adverbs for the sentences and to look for adverbs in 'Escape'. Try reading the paragraph without the adverbs. Talk about how the adverbs help to improve the description.

Horoscope adverbs

- Each zodiac sign on this chart has three **adverbs** to describe people born under that sign. Discuss how accurately they describe your friends and relations. Think of other adverbs that describe them more accurately.
- Use suitable adverbs from this chart to describe a character you are reading about or to create a character for a story you are writing. Use a separate page.

22 March–20 April	21 April–21 May	22 May–22 June
 An **ARIES** acts: bravely, enthusiastically, boastfully	A **TAURUS** acts: patiently, kindly, clumsily	A **GEMINI** acts: artistically, generously, wastefully
23 June–23 July	24 July–23 August	24 August–23 September
 A **CANCER** acts: kindly, helpfully, moodily	A **LEO** acts: cheerfully, loyally, big-headedly	A **VIRGO** acts: honestly, charmingly, nervously
24 September–23 October	24 October–22 November	23 November–22 December
 A **LIBRA** acts: sensibly, truthfully, lazily	A **SCORPIO** acts: methodically, cautiously, secretively	 A **SAGITTARIUS** acts: happily, cleverly, proudly
23 December–19 January	20 January–19 February	20 February–21 March
 A **CAPRICORN** acts: strongly, orderly, gloomily	 An **AQUARIUS** acts: friendly, calmly, dreamily	A **PISCES** acts: lovingly, romantically, lazily

Dear Helper,

Objective: to revise adverbs.

Discuss how different adverbs apply to different people that you and your child know. Use the chart as a starting point.

Cluttered desk

An important use of the **comma** is to divide up lists of words:

Example: I went to the shop and bought a box of cornflakes, a jar of jam,
a packet of tea, a loaf of bread and a tub of ice-cream.

Notice that a comma is usually not required before the final item in a list because the word **and** is used to join the last item.

● Complete these sentences with lists based on what you can see in the picture. Don't forget to add **a** or **an** where needed and to use commas.

My desk was cluttered with

_____

_____

_____

For my birthday I'm hoping to get

_____

_____

_____

When I go to secondary school I will be studying

_____

_____

_____

In the toolbox there was

_____

_____

_____

Dear Helper,

Objective: to practise using commas in lists.

Help your child to identify the items in the pictures, add suitable determiners (a, an, some etc.), put commas in the right places, and use 'and' to join the last item. Talk about how commas (and other punctuation) help to make sentences easier to understand.

Character quotes

- Choose one of the main characters from a story you are reading and describe the character with evidence from the text. Use the table below to help you.

Description of characteristics Describe the following characteristics in your own words.	Evidence from text Quote words, phrases or sentences as evidence for your description. Enclose in quotation marks.
Appearance	
Personality	
Relationship with others	
Important actions	

Dear Helper,

Objective: to identify the main characteristics of characters, drawing on the text to justify views.

Ask your child to describe the character to you and, as they do so, help them identify which aspect of the left-hand column it belongs in. Encourage them to find something to say for each aspect. Then help your child to look through the story to find quotable evidence to support their description.

Story order

They had not gone far when their jeep was stopped by a tree which had fallen across the trail. As soon as they got out to move it, they found themselves surrounded by bandits with AK47 rifles. Tom groaned, and Lindsey wept – but Paco laughed. He knew these men, and after a few words in Spanish, and the gift of a bottle of whisky, they were on their way again.

Tom had heard the legend of the 'Dinosaurs on Dinosaur Plateau' and decided that he would like to be the first to bring back a real dinosaur egg. So he gave up his job as a Geography teacher and set out with his wife, Lindsey, for Porto Paso.

After a difficult climb, they reached the Plateau. There was a movement in bushes ahead, and a creature lifted its head to look at them. The head was huge, scaly and had rows of sharp teeth.
'A dinosaur!' shouted Tom.
'No,' said Lindsey sadly, 'only a monitor lizard'.

Tom got his old job back teaching Geography, and though his adventure did not make him rich, it gave him a rich fund of stories to tell to his pupils.

When they arrived in Porto Paso, they bought a jeep and supplies for a month. Hiring a local guide was more difficult. They seemed afraid of bandits, gorillas and hostile tribes – but most of all, of the dinosaurs that they thought were living on the plateau. At last they found an old man who agreed to be their guide. His name was Paco.

- Cut out the jumbled up paragraphs above. Arrange them into the correct order and stick them on another piece of paper. Label each paragraph with one of the following headings:
  - Introduction
  - Build up
  - Conflict
  - Climax
  - Resolution

Dear Helper,

Objective: to sequence a story and identify its main stages.
Make sure that your child reads the paragraphs carefully before attempting to re-assemble them. Discuss with them what helped them decide on the correct order.

Name:

All in good time

- Read this playscript and prepare it for performance.
- Write an extra scene about what happens next week.

Mrs Scratchit:	This week, we are going to be studying a masterpiece of classic literature.
Billy:	Oh no!
Mrs Scratchit:	It's called *The Time Machine* by H.G. Wells. And to help us understand what it is about, my brother has made this working model of a time machine from the description in the book. (*Billy looks interested.*)
Kirsty and Karen:	Oh no!
Mrs Scratchit:	Pay attention! Now, this lever here is used to go back into the past. (*She pulls the lever.*)
Billy:	(*Running to the window*) Hey, look, that tree is shrinking!
Karen:	(*Looking towards the road*) Where are all the cars?
Kirsty:	Why are there knights in armour on the school field?
Billy:	(*Realising what has happened*) It actually works!
Kirsty and Karen:	What works?
Billy:	That model time machine!
Karen:	Miss, it works! It works!
Kirsty:	Can we go to Ancient Egypt?
Karen:	Can we see the dinosaurs?
Mrs Scratchit:	How dare you interrupt my lesson! I thought I told you — this week we are studying classic literature.
Billy:	But what about the time machine?
Mrs Scratchit:	(*Unimpressed*) All in good time. If you work hard on the novel, I may consider taking you to Ancient Egypt next week.

Dear Helper,

Objective: to prepare, read and perform a playscript.
Read the playscript with your child and discuss how it could be prepared for performance. Discuss ideas for writing an extra scene.

Two eagle poems

- Read these two poems and discuss their similarities and differences.

The Eagle

He clasps the crag with crooked hands;
Close to the sun in lonely lands,
Ringed with the azure world, he stands.

The wrinkled sea beneath him crawls;
He watches from his mountain walls,
And like a thunderbolt he falls.

Alfred Lord Tennyson (1809–1892)

crag = cliff; azure = blue

eagle

eagle
majestic appearance
power of flight,
king of birds

since ancient times symbol
of strength and courage
Sumerians 5000 years ago
Imperial Rome
America

but a killer
a dive bomber
with laser sights
that always hits its target

Malcolm George (1950–)

Sumerians = ancient inhabitants of the Tigris-Euphrates valley

Dear Helper,

Objective: to compare and contrast poems on similar themes.
Share the reading of these poems with your child, then discuss their similarities and differences.

Poem v poem

● Use this frame to help you compare and contrast two poems on similar themes. Use the back of this page if you require more space.

	Title	Title
Subject What does the poet say about the chosen subject? In what way do the poets treat the subject differently?		
Verse Form Is it rhymed verse or free verse? Is there a regular rhythm? Is it set out in verses?		
Vocabulary Jot down any interesting or unusual words and say why they are effective.		
Figures of speech Give an example of a simile or metaphor used by the poet and say why it is effective.		
Preference Which poem did you most enjoy reading and why?		

Dear Helper,

Objective: to compare and contrast poems on similar themes.

Your child will have been given two poems to compare and contrast. Share the reading of the poems with your child, then discuss each of the sections in the table and help your child to complete it.

Dinosaur Plateau

- Plan a story based on this map. Your adventure should start in Porto Paso. Your quest is to get to Dinosaur Plateau and bring back some dinosaur eggs or baby dinosaurs which are worth a small fortune.

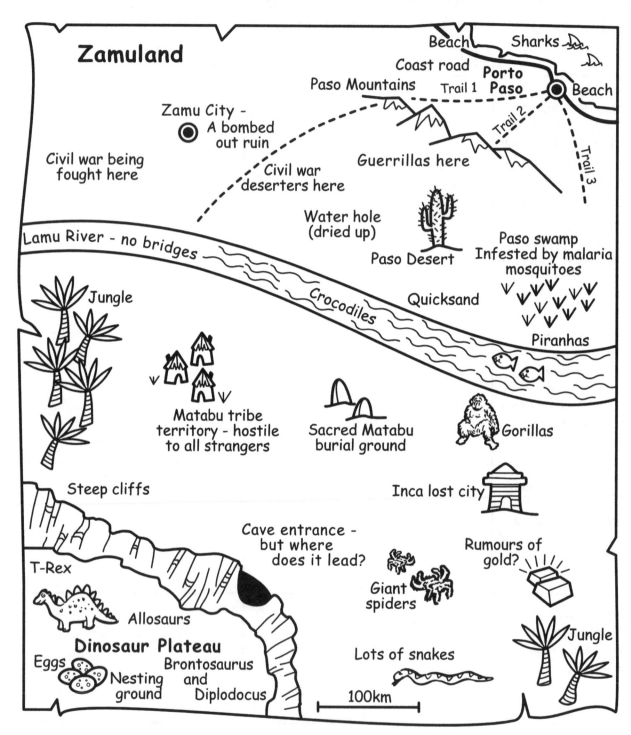

Dear Helper,

Objective: to use different ways of planning stories.

Discuss the map with your child, and the kind of adventures that explorers would have if they tried to get to the plateau. Help your child to make a paragraph plan, in which each paragraph describes a stage of the journey, an adventure or an incident.

Pantomime planner

● Use this planning page to give you some ideas for a modern pantomime. Write an outline for your pantomime on the back of this page.

Popular pantos

● Choose one of these popular pantomimes. You could also have fun by choosing more than one and mixing up the plots. For example, what would happen if Little Red Riding Hood found Sleeping Beauty in Grandma's bed?

- Aladdin
- Little Red Riding Hood
- Sleeping Beauty
- Cinderella
- Snow White
- Hansel and Gretel

Stereotype breakers

● Include one or more of the following to make your pantomime modern and different.

Characters
- A rapping prince
- A tough princess
- An alien
- A genetically modified plant

Settings
- A burger bar
- A football stadium
- Another planet
- A car factory

Objects
- A computer
- A mobile phone
- A sports car
- A guitar

Dear Helper,

Objective: to write a playscript using known stories as a basis.

Help your child to remember the stories of the popular pantomimes, and then discuss how to make it modern and different. Use the ideas on the planner or some of their own..

T

Monty mouse

Rules for writing paragraphs

A new paragraph is shown by an **indentation** of approximately 1cm from the margin (except for the first paragraph, which starts at the margin).
Do not leave whole blank lines between paragraphs.
In stories, start a new paragraph for each big step forward in the plot.

- Use the rules above and the paragraph plan below to help you to write a story in paragraphs.
  Use a separate piece of paper.

Monty Mouse lived happily in grandma's house...

- Describe Monty, his comfortable mouse hole, and how he lived.

One day, he looked out of his mouse hole and saw – a cat!

- Describe the cat which Grandma has just bought and how Monty feels about it.

Things went from bad to worse when...

- Describe how the cat nearly caught him. This paragraph should have lots of exciting description.

Monty realised that he would have to get rid of that cat, so he sat down to think up a plan...

- Explain Monty's plan.

The day came when his plan was going to be put into action...

- Describe how the plan works. This paragraph is the climax of the story. It should be full of excitement. The reader should be kept in suspense until the last moment about whether the plan will work.

Peace at last...

- End the story by describing how Monty settles happily into his old routine.

Dear Helper,

Objective: to use paragraphs in story writing.
When your child is writing the story, help them by checking that the rules of paragraphing are being followed correctly.

The resort of the millennium

- Read this article, then find and underline examples of: **headings**, **lists**, **bullet points**, **captions**.
- Discuss how these features help you to find information more easily.

PORTO PASO

Porto Paso is a city with a large harbour, and a good road leading along the coast to other major cities. It has wonderful weather all year round and some of the best beaches in the world, but at the moment, very few tourists go there. That is about to change.

Tourism

Porto Paso could be the tourist resort of the millennium. Among its advantages are:

- wonderful weather all year round
- some of the best beaches in the world
- near to a lost Inca city
- near to Dinosaur Plateau

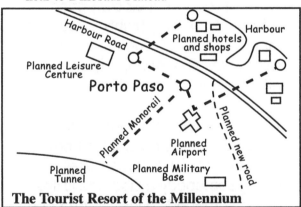

The Tourist Resort of the Millennium

The Porto Paso development plan

2002 Develop the beaches and drive away the sharks.

2003 Explore Dinosaur Plateau and the lost Inca city.

2004 Build an airport at Porto Paso.

2006 Build a monorail to the Plateau and the Inca city.

2008 Build hotels, shops, restaurants, etc. for tourists.

'Extinct'? The Government hope not!

Dinosaurs

It is the dinosaurs that will bring the tourists flocking in. There are stories that dinosaurs have survived on a plateau about 400km to the south of Porto Paso. The government is planning an expedition to explore the plateau. If the reports are true, they expect that Porto Paso will be one of the richest cities in the world by the year 2010.

Holiday of a lifetime

Dear Helper,

Objective: to identify features of non-fiction texts: headings, lists, bullet points, captions.

Help your child to find and underline the features listed above. Then, find a real magazine or newspaper, and look for the features there.

Name:

A loaded gun?

- Read this article about smoking. Highlight **facts** in one colour and **opinions** in another.

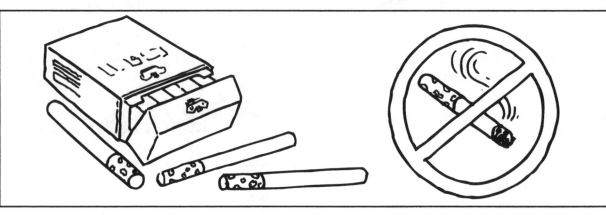

A loaded gun?

Cigarette smoking causes lung cancer. This has been proved by scientists. Smoking is a disgusting habit. Smokers' breaths smell foul and their clothes smell stale. What is worse, they pollute the atmosphere for others. Smoking is already banned in many public places, and I believe that there should be a total ban. Smoking tobacco should be made illegal – like drugs. After all, that is what tobacco is – a dangerous drug.

Scientific tests show that there are over 60 dangerous substances in tobacco smoke. Two of the most dangerous are carbon monoxide and tar. Carbon monoxide is a poison – it is the stuff that pours out of car exhaust pipes, and tar gums up the lungs.

Smoking by a pregnant woman increases the risks of miscarriage, low birth weight, and death of the newborn baby. We should therefore stop smokers for their own good. Tobacco is already highly taxed, but I think that the government should raise taxes so that nobody can afford tobacco.

The risk of dying from lung cancer is 20 to 30 times greater for a heavy smoker than for a non-smoker. So giving somebody a cigarette is like giving somebody a loaded gun and asking them to turn it on themselves and pull the trigger.

Dear Helper,

Objective: to distinguish between fact and opinion.

Read the passage with your child, then ask them to highlight the *facts* first as they are easiest to find. Then, highlight statements which are clearly *opinions*. This will leave several statements left over which will have to be considered more carefully.

PORTO PASO TIMES

GUERRILLAS DRIVEN BACK

Porto Paso is now free from terrorist attack

Zamu guerrilla fighters have been driven back by government forces to the far side of the Paso mountains. The last pocket of resistance – where Trail 3 approaches the mountains – was cleared yesterday by soldiers of the 4th Battalion. Now that Porto Paso is free from terrorist attack, the government hopes that the economy can be built up. They believe that tourism is Porto Paso's best chance for future development.

A group a soldiers hold victory flag aloft

WEATHER

High pressure means that the temperatures will continue at around 36°C for the next few days. Rain is not expected for several weeks, and travellers should beware that many waterholes in the Paso Desert have dried up.

Today Hot and sunny	
Tuesday Very warm some breeze	
Wednesday Hot and sunny	
Thursday Warm very little breeze	
Friday Slightly cooler day	

TOURIST PLANS

The government plans to increase the number of tourists visiting Porto Paso from 17 this year to 10 000 in ten years' time.

A government spokesman said that this was a realistic target because Porto Paso has some of the best beaches in the world. See our Tourism Plans supplement on page 6.

Porto Paso North Beach

Advertisements

PHOTOCOPIABLE

Name: _____

Newspaper features

- Use this chart to compare two newspapers.

	Name _____	Name _____
Layout & Organisation Size of newspaper. How many columns? How many pictures per page? Use of colour? Type of font? Size of headlines and subheadings.		
Range of information What topics are included, eg home news, world news, weather, finance, sport, etc.		
Voice Who is writing? Which articles are anonymous? Which are by a named writer? Which are written by the editor? Which are written by advertisers?		
Formality Is the tone of the news paper friendly, formal (ie, impersonal tone, big words, long sentences) or in between?		

Dear Helper,

Objective: to identify the main features of newspapers.

Provide your child with two different newspapers (a broadsheet and a tabloid would be ideal). Alternatively, compare one newspaper with the simulated newspaper page your child has brought home. Discuss the features and look for examples in each of the papers.

Headline news

- Write a short article to go with each of these headlines. Note that they are based on the information given in the article *The resort of the millennium*, which comes with this activity.

DISAPPOINTMENT ON DINOSAUR PLATEAU

SHARK ATTACK ON PORTO PASO'S NORTH BEACH

Extension

- Write further articles using the headlines below. Use the back of this page.

  PORTO PASO TOURIST PLANS A DISASTER

  LOST INCA CITY A 'MYTH' SAYS HISTORIAN

  PORTO PASO AIRPORT BEHIND SCHEDULE

Dear Helper,

Objective: to predict newspaper stories from the evidence of headlines.

Read *The resort of the millennium* with your child. Then predict and make notes for the above newspaper stories from the headlines. Then try it on a real newspaper!

Easy-tent

- Underline the following key features in the instructions below using different coloured pens: **list of materials, sequential stages, language of commands** (underline all **imperative verbs**).

How to set up your tent

1 Check that you have everything you need:

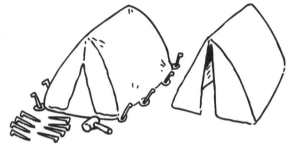

The green outer tent
The white inner tent
The super pump
Fully charged batteries
8 large plastic pegs

2 Connect the super pump to the inlet valve on the green outer tent by removing the red cap, and screwing the plastic hose into position.

3

Switch on the super pump. After about five minutes, the green outer tent should have risen to a dome shape. When this is firm and round, switch off the pump and remove the plastic hose. A one-way valve will stop the air escaping, but remember to replace the red cap just to make sure! NOTE: if the pump fails or the batteries go flat, you will find an emergency nozzle near the inlet valve. Use this to blow up the tent by mouth.

4 **Important:** Immediately peg the green tent to the ground by placing pegs through ALL of the eight loops. The EASY-TENT is very light and may get blown away if you forget to do this!

5 Place the white inner tent inside the green outer tent and pump up in the same way.

6 Your EASY-TENT is now ready. Enjoy your holiday!

- Write a set of instructions for an everyday object. You can use the back of this page.

Dear Helper,

Objective: to identify features of instructions.

Your child will find that the hardest part of this homework is finding the imperative verbs. Help them to do this. An imperative verb is easily recognised because it has no subject (eg 'Check' instead of 'You check'). Most of the numbered stages begin with imperative verbs. Help your child decide on a suitable everyday object for which instructions can be written.

Be a newspaper editor

- Your reporter has given you this rough draft of an article. It is nearly 300 words long, but you only have space for 150. Edit it down to size, and divide it into paragraphs. Use a separate page for your summary.

Suggestions:

- Leave out a whole section (eg the background information on monitor lizards, Dr Ricard's description of the first sighting, the information about the Inca city).
- Shorten each section as much as possible by including only essential information.
- Divide the final article into two or three paragraphs.

The expedition to Dinosaur Plateau returned yesterday. But it brings both good news and bad. The good news is that the dinosaurs do exist — in a way. The team found a new species of giant monitor lizard living on the plateau. The bad news is that giant monitor lizards may not be enough to attract tourists. Biologist Dr Paul Ricard, who is Professor of Biology at Panana University, described his first sight of the beasts. 'We were hacking through the jungle with our machetes when I saw a huge scaly head rise above the undergrowth. At first I thought it was a real dinosaur, but when we got closer, I could tell that it was just a huge lizard.' The scientific name for the monitor lizard is Lacertilia Varanidae. Monitor lizards like water, and are often found near lakes. They feed on eggs, fishes and molluscs. They lay eggs on dry land and can live for up to fifteen years. The largest species of monitor lizard in other parts of the world can grow to more than two metres in length. The monitor lizards on Dinosaur Plateau are nearly twice this size, and for this reason Dr Ricard named them ' Lacertilia Varanidae Dinosauria', which means 'Terrible Monitor Lizard'. Another piece of bad news is that the lost Inca city is so badly ruined that it is just a pile of rubble. The government hopes that it will be possible to go ahead with tourist development anyway. They are pleased that Dr Ricard included the word 'Dinosauria' in his new scientific name for the lizards, as they will be able to advertise the lizards as 'Dinosaur Lizards' without breaking any laws.

Dear Helper,

Objective: to edit a newspaper story to fit a particular space.

Read the rough draft of the article with your child and discuss what could be left out to make it fit the 150 word space.

Driving guide

Instructions must always be clear and in the correct order.

- Place the instructions for **Setting off** in the correct order by numbering them.
- Complete the 'Driving Guide' by writing similar instructions in the box for 'Traffic Lights' and 'Overtaking'.

Setting off

As the car gains speed, change gear until you are in top gear.

Check in the mirror.

Check that the car is in neutral gear.

Check that the handbrake is on.

Engage first gear.

Get in the car.

If all is clear, release the handbrake, and pull out.

Put your seatbelt on.

Start the engine.

Traffic Lights

Overtaking

Dear Helper,

Objective: to write clear instructions.

Help your child by providing information about driving and rules of the road.

Porto Paso report

- Imagine that you are the chairperson of the Porto Paso development committee. The year is 2009, and you are writing your annual report based on the six headings below. Complete your report using these headings. The first has been done for you.

1. Develop the beaches and drive away the sharks

Toilets and restaurants have been built on North and South beaches, and a new bus service provided (until the monorail is finished). However, the shark control boats are finding it difficult to get rid of the sharks.

2. Explore Dinosaur Plateau and the lost Inca city

3. Build an airport at Porto Paso

4. Build a monorail to the Plateau and the lost Inca city

5. Build hotels, shops, restaurants for tourists

6. Will we be ready for 2010?

Dear Helper,

Objective: to write a report.

Read *The resort of the millennium* with your child and discuss what problems might have come up that should be included in the report.

Name:

Chefs and chiefs

The plural of most words ending in **f** or **fe** is formed by changing **f** or **fe** to **v** and adding **es**: eg **wife, wives**.

Learn these exceptions: **beliefs, chefs, chiefs, clefs, reefs, roofs**.

● Complete the table by writing the plural forms.

Singular	Plural
belief	beliefs
calf	
chef	
chief	
clef	
dwarf	
elf	
half	
hoof	
knife	
leaf	
loaf	
reef	
roof	
safe	
scarf	
self	
sheaf	
shelf	
thiefs	
wharf	
wife	
wolf	

Dear Helper,

Objective: to learn plural forms of words ending in -f or -fe.

Help your child to memorise the list of exceptions to the spelling rule. Try making up a nonsense sentence to remember them. Here's one: *The chief chef stands on the roof and shouts his belief that the treble clef and a coral reef have much in common.* Check that your child does not forget them when completing the table.

100 LITERACY HOMEWORK ACTIVITIES • YEAR 4 TERM 2

Damsel in distress

- Complete the words in the first and third column by adding **-ight** or **-ite** alongside them. The first one has been done for you.

appet	ite	l	
b		m	
bl		midn	
br		n	
dayl		pol	
del		r	
exc		rec	
f		sl	
fl		sp	
goodn		t	
he		twil	
ign		un	
inv		watert	
k		wh	
kn		wr	

- Find suitable rhyming words to complete the poem below.

One evening, Henry wrote a poem
About a gallant _____,
Who saved a damsel in distress
And got into a _____.

It was a dragon that he fought,
Whose breath made fires _____,
But he put on a fire-proof coat
And so his wounds were _____.

Extension

- Try writing a rhyming poem of your own using the words above. Use the back of this page.

Dear Helper,

Objective: to learn to spell words with the endings *-ight* and *-ite*.

Remind your child that the two letter sequences *-ight* and *-ite* have the same sound but are used in different words. Check that your child completes the table with the correct letter sequence. Help them find words that rhyme and make sense for the poem. Playing with rhyme helps spelling, so encourage your child to try writing their own poem.

Got a nice garden

- Rewrite each of these sentences with a different adjective in place of **nice**:

We have a nice garden. _____

What a nice day! _____

I'm reading a nice book. _____

I want to live in a nice house. _____

Mr Jones is a very nice man. _____

I'd like a nice cup of tea. _____

- Rewrite each of these sentences with a different verb in place of **got**. Note that it is sometimes better to rewrite the whole sentence. For example, the first sentence could be rewritten as *Look at my Christmas presents!*

Look what I got for Christmas! _____

He got up at 7 am. _____

Susan got a bad cold from her brother. _____

My computer's got a DVD drive. _____

Jason got to school just in time. _____

What have you got there? _____

Dear Helper,

Objective: to use alternative words to *got* and *nice*.

It is important that children understand that there is nothing wrong with the words *nice* and *got* – they are perfectly correct English. However, they are overused. Help your child to think of alternative words. Note that, to avoid using *got*, sentences sometimes have to be reworded.

Where's my partner?

Some words tell you the **gender** of the person or animal they describe. They tell you if it is male or female. The suffix **-ess** indicates that the word is feminine.

- Match up the masculine and feminine forms of the following words. The first one has been done for you.

Masculine	Feminine
actor	lioness
author	baroness
baron	authoress
duke	hostess
enchanter	instructress
god	manageress
heir	poetess
host	actress
instructor	mistress
lion	princess
manager	shepherdess
master	sorceress
murderer	tigress
poet	waitress
priest	duchess
prince	priestess
shepherd	enchantress
sorcerer	goddess
tiger	heiress
waiter	murderess

- In these days of equal opportunity, some feminine words are rarely used. Highlight these words in the above list.

Dear Helper,

Objective: to explore gender suffixes.
The matching task is easy. However, your child may need help to identify those feminine forms which are rarely used today.

Who's my partner?

Some words tell you the **gender** of the person or animal they describe. They tell you if it is male or female.

- Write the feminine forms of the masculine words in the second column. The first one is done for you.

Masculine	Feminine
bachelor	spinster
boy	
brother	
bull	
dog	
gander	
gentleman	
groom	
hero	
husband	
king	
male	
monk	
Mr	
nephew	
ram	
sir	
stallion	
uncle	
wizard	

- In these days of equal opportunity, some feminine words are rarely used. Highlight these words in the above list.

Dear Helper,

Objective: to explore gender-specific words.

Your child may need help with the feminine forms of some words, eg nephew.

Name:

Arseling-pole

● Investigate these archaic words by highlighting in different colours:
  - words for jobs which no longer exist;
  - words for things which are no longer used;
  - words for things which still exist, but which have been replaced by a new word.

You may find a dictionary helpful.

Archaic word	Meaning
arseling-pole	a pole used by bakers to move hot ashes
bakester	a female baker
beadle	a keeper of an alms house or prison
cockler	a seller of cockles
colic	a cough or cold
farrier	a blacksmith
fortepiano	a piano
gramophone	a record player
ice chest	used to keep food cool before refrigerators
keel-alley	a bowling alley
kissing-comfits	sugar plums (used to sweeten the breath)
magic lantern	an early type of projector
moonling	a lunatic
ostler	a stableman at an inn
pantry	a room in which food is stored
parlour	the best room in the house
phonograph	the earliest type of recording machine
radiogram	a record player and radio combined
stenographer	a person who writes shorthand
telegraph	sends messages in morse code
topless	excellent
ugsome	ugly
wireless	radio
yammer	cry loudly
zoetrope	a toy which displays moving pictures

Dear Helper,

Objective: to understand that vocabulary changes over time.

Read and enjoy this list of archaic words with your child, then help them to investigate it, by highlighting different kinds of words in different colours. Can you think of any more archaic words that your child can add to the list? Remind your child to look out for old words and expressions in their reading.

PHOTOCOPIABLE

Glossary

- Use this glossary for further study of the ballad *Robin and Gandelyn*.

ME = Middle English. This is a very old version of the English language spoken from about 1100 until about 1500 (before that, Anglo-Saxon was spoken).

carping	(ME) speaking
clerk	educated person
lyeth	lies (the '-th' suffix was used until about 100 years ago to show the third person singular)
bounden	imprisoned in death
mickle	(ME) large
stalked	crept up
cleaving	cutting
y-flayed,	(ME) skinned ('-y' is a prefix which was used in ME to show the past tense)
eke	(ME) yet
ere	when
clepen	(ME) called
dost	do you (the '-st' suffix was used to show the second person singular)
thou hast	you have
thy	your
slain	killed
ye	you (plural – compare with 'thou' which is singular)

- Write a modern translation of the poem in simple prose. Use the back of this page
- Give an approximate date for the poem. Is it older or more recent than Shakespeare's plays? How can you tell?

Dear Helper,

Objective: to understand that vocabulary changes over time.

Help your child to use the glossary to write a simple modern translation of the poem. Use the information in the glossary – and any background knowledge about Robin Hood – to estimate the date of the ballad.

Enjoyable, delightful, childlike

- Turn the **nouns** and **verbs** in the first column into **adjectives** by adding one of the following suffixes:

-able   -ful   -like

Note: most words add the suffix without change. Take care with **beauty** and **love**.

Noun or verb	Adjective
arm	armful
beauty	
break	
business	
change	
colour	
comfort	
doubt	
drink	
ear	
help	
joy	
lady	
life	
like	
love	
power	
read	
success	
war	

Dear Helper,

Objective: to explore word endings that turn nouns and verbs into adjectives: -able, -ful, -like.
Help your child add the appropriate suffix. Generally, this is simply a matter of common sense, of what sounds right.

Shocking, dynamic, newsworthy!

• Turn the **nouns** and **verbs** in the first column into **adjectives** by adding one of the following suffixes:

-ing   -ic   -worthy

Note: some words add the suffix without change, others drop the final **e**.

Noun or verb	Adjective
ache	aching
adore	
agonise	
air	
alcohol	
artist	
astonish	
bawl	
blaze	
bleed	
boil	
bore	
cube	
enthusiast	
hero	
idiot	
magnet	
praise	
sea	
telescope	

Dear Helper,

Objective: to explore word endings that turn nouns and verbs into adjectives: *-ing, -ic, -worthy*.

Help your child add the appropriate suffix. Generally, this is simply a matter of common sense, of what sounds right – but take care with words ending in e!

Fussy werewolf

An **adjective** is a describing word. It describes the noun it goes with.

Examples: The horse pulls a **heavy** load.

The **gruesome** creature kissed me.

That mountain is **high**.

- Fill the gaps in the passage below with suitable **adjectives**.

The werewolf climbed in through the ＿＿＿＿＿＿ window.

He saw a ＿＿＿＿＿＿ cot where a ＿＿＿＿＿＿ baby was sleeping.

He bared his ＿＿＿＿＿＿ teeth in a ＿＿＿＿＿＿ snarl and crept

towards the cot. He paused to look at the baby. She had ＿＿＿＿＿＿

hair, her eyes were ＿＿＿＿＿＿, and she was wearing a

＿＿＿＿＿＿ sleep suit and a ＿＿＿＿＿＿ nappy. Suddenly, the

werewolf noticed a ＿＿＿＿＿＿ smell. The baby's nappy needed

changing!

'Yuck!' grunted the werewolf, 'I prefer

＿＿＿＿＿＿ food!'

Dear Helper,

Objective: to revise adjectives.

Help your child to fill the gaps in the passage by checking to see that each one is an adjective.

Horoscope adjectives

- Each zodiac sign on this chart has three adjectives to describe people born under that sign. Discuss how accurately they describe your friends and relations. Think of other adjectives that describe them more accurately.
- Use suitable adjectives from this chart to describe a character you are reading about or to create a character for a story you are writing. Use a separate page.

22 March–20 April	21 April–21 May	22 May–22 June
 An **ARIES** is: energetic, courageous but can be bad-tempered	A **TAURUS** is: good, honourable but can be argumentative	A **GEMINI** is: charming, sensitive but can be clumsy
23 June–23 July	24 July–23 August	24 August–23 September
A **CANCER** is: loyal, generous but can be miserable	A **LEO** is: ambitious, daring but can be reckless	A **VIRGO** is: intelligent, hard-working but can be
24 September–23 October	24 October–22 November	23 November–22 December
 A **LIBRA** is: kind, adaptable but can be vain	A **SCORPIO** is: scientific, thorough but can be suspicious	A **SAGITTARIUS** is: sporting, honest but can be critical
23 December–19 January	20 January–19 February	20 February–21 March
A **CAPRICORN** is: strong-minded, disciplined but can be moody	 An **AQUARIUS** is: artistic, truthful but can be petty	A **PISCES** is: imaginative, warm but can be scatterbrained

Dear Helper,

Objective: to revise adjectives.

Discuss how different adjectives apply to different people that you and your child know. Encourage your child to build up a bank of character adjectives to draw on when writing stories.

Carry my case

Adjectives are used to describe and compare things.

The **positive** is used to describe something: *I have a **heavy** suitcase.*
The **comparative** is used to compare two things: *My suitcase is **heavier** than yours.*
The **superlative** is used when comparing three or more things: *Susan's suitcase is the **heaviest** of all.*

Note that some adjectives add the endings **-er** and **-est**, others add the words **more** and **most**.

● Sort the adjectives into their correct cases: **positive**, **comparative** or **superlative**.

kind	more intelligent	quietest	quiet
loyal	greenest	greener	more charming
green	most loyal	most charming	quieter
kindest	warmest	kinder	warmer
more loyal	intelligent	charming	warm
			most intelligent

Positive
heavy   selfish

Superlative
heaviest
most selfish

Comparative
heavier   more selfish

Dear Helper,

Objective: to examine adjectives used for comparison.

Help your child to sort the adjectives into the correct suitcases. To ensure your child understands the terms *comparative* and *superlative*, ask them to use some of the words in a sentence.

Oddly shaped

An **adjectival phrase** is a group of words which acts like an adjective.

       Examples: The clown was **very funny**.
                 Who is the girl **with the long hair?**

- Choose suitable **adjectival phrases** from the list below to fill the gaps in the sentences.

of average height
oddly shaped
strangely disturbing
too cold
too small
very exciting
with the computer
worth reading

The book on the table is_____.

The classrooms in the new block are _____.

The new Super 10 is an _____ car.

The suspect is a man _____.

That film was _____.

James is the boy _____.

I found the book _____.

The food on the table is _____.

Dear Helper,

Objective: to construct adjectival phrases.

The term *adjectival phrase* may sound difficult, but adjectival phrases are used naturally by all of us. Reassure your child about this, and encourage them to complete the task using common sense, ie what sounds right.

Name:

Jason's lipstick

Object cards

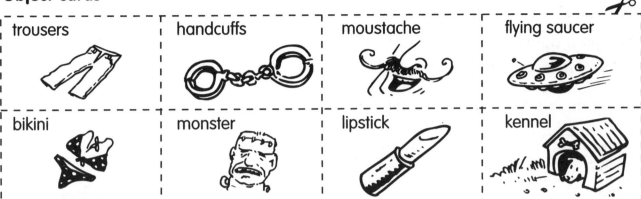

trousers | handcuffs | moustache | flying saucer

bikini | monster | lipstick | kennel

Owner cards

Jason | The policeman | Mr Smith | The alien

Susan | Dr Frankenstein | Mrs Green | Rover

The **possessive apostrophe** is used to show ownership.
Example: Rover's mobile phone was attached to his collar.

- Play the 'Apostrophe game'. Here's how:
  - Cut out the cards and put them into two sets, **object** and **owner**.
  - Shuffle each set and place them face down.
  - One player chooses a card from each set and gives them to the other player.
  - The other player has to write out a sentence like the example above using the words on the cards. If it is written correctly, they win a point.
  - The players take turns. The player with the most points at the end is the winner.

Dear Helper,

Objective: to use the apostrophe accurately to mark possession.

Play the 'Apostrophe game' with your child. Check that they write full sentences which begin with a capital letter, use the apostrophe correctly and have a full stop at the end.

Cat o' nine tails

An **apostrophe** is used to show where letters have been missed out of a word. The shortened forms are called **contractions**.

Examples: do not = **don't**   is not = **isn't**   might have = **might've**

cat of nine tails = **cat o' nine tails**   of the clock = **o'clock**

- Complete the gaps in the table. The first one has been done as an example.

Long form	Shortened form
he will	he'll
I am	
they have	
she is	
we are	
you had	
he will	
I would	
	they're
	Tom's
	can't
	it's
	won't
	shouldn't
	I'd
	didn't

- Read the paragraph below. Write the **contractions** above the words in bold.

It was nearly 10 **of the clock** and **I had** still not finished my homework. If

I **did not** hand it in the next day, my teacher **would not** be pleased. 'I know,' I

thought to myself. '**I will** go to bed and leave my books on the desk. Maybe an

elf will come in the night and do it for me!'

Dear Helper,

Objective: to use the apostrophe to show contraction.
Help to ensure that your child has put the apostrophe in the right place.

Imaginary worlds

Crumbling Cave	Deep Dark Forest	Dragon	Dwarves' Mine
Elixir of Life	Fortress of Doom	Goblin	Imprisoned Princess
Magic Mirror	Murky Mire	Mysterious Museum	Prince's Palace
Treasure Chest	Wicked Wizard	Witch	Witch's Hovel

- Cut out the small pictures above and paste them on a sheet of paper to create a map of a fantasy world. Add larger details such as roads, rivers, mountain ranges, etc. Add your own ideas.

Dear Helper,

Objective: to understand how writers create imaginary worlds.

Discuss each picture and how it could be used on a map. Note that some of the cards, such as the Treasure Chest can be used as motives for a story line and the creatures can be used as hazards. As the map takes shape, discuss possible stories that could grow out of it, and work out detailed descriptions of places, people and objects.

Name:

Alien in the mall

- Think of settings in which you might find these characters.
- Choose one or two characters and think of different or unusual settings in which they might be placed.
- Make notes about how the characters would behave differently in these unusual settings. Use a separate sheet.

Dear Helper,

Objective: to understand how settings influence characters' behaviour.

Help your child to explore how different settings would affect different characters. For example, if an alien landed on a desert island, he might think that earth was an uninhabited planet; if he landed at a theme park, people might think he was an entertainer in a costume.

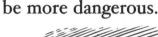
Land of snow-capped mountains

- Compare and contrast the settings in the six passages below. Highlight **adjectives** and **figures of speech** in different colours. Write a note about the kind of story that might take place in each setting.

It is a land of snow-capped mountains and dense dark pine forests; a land where the Aurora Borealis flickers like a Christmas light show; a land where the timber wolf howls all night; a land where bitter cold stabs like a knife – and can be more dangerous.

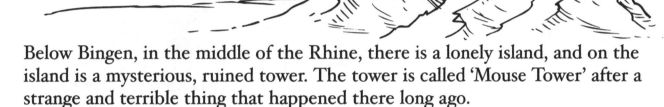

Below Bingen, in the middle of the Rhine, there is a lonely island, and on the island is a mysterious, ruined tower. The tower is called 'Mouse Tower' after a strange and terrible thing that happened there long ago.

✳ ✳ ✳

Here at last! Billidorm! From my hotel window I can see the golden beaches and the crystal clear sea. I can't wait to get out there – trouble is, I think I've got a touch of Spanish tummy!

✳ ✳ ✳

Our village school was small and old fashioned. The classrooms had high ceilings and high windows. Each desk had a small hole for an inkwell, and fresh ink was given out every morning. The teacher's desk stood on a raised platform, and next to it stood our teacher, like a captain on the bridge.

✳ ✳ ✳

'Mega Mall' is the largest shopping centre in the north. It has every shop you have ever heard of, and many others which you haven't. If you are a dedicated shopper, like I am, you will think you have died and gone to heaven.

Zeta is a planet much like earth – though with less water. Much of the land is dry, stony desert. The night sky is spectacular as Zeta is a planet with rings like Saturn. It also has two moons, one of which is nearly as big as Earth's.

Dear Helper,

Objective: to compare and contrast settings across a range of stories.
Share the reading of these story settings with your child. Look for adjectives and other descriptive expressions that help you visualise the setting. Discuss the kind of story that might take place in each setting.

PHOTOCOPIABLE

Name:

See, saw, stegosaur

A **simile** is a comparison using **like** or **as**.

- Read the poem and highlight or underline the **similes**.

Hello, I'm pleased to meet you,
My back is like a saw,
But don't use me for cutting wood
'Cause I'm a stegosaur.

Now, if you think you're overweight,
Don't worry, I weigh more
(As much as ten 10-ton big trucks)
'Cause I'm a brontosaur.

I'm a pterodactyl-
A bat, a bird? - Not quite!
I'm nothing like a bird at all,
More like a leather kite.

And if you think you're rather sharp
Just look into my jaw:
My teeth are like a row of knives,
'Cause I'm a tyrannosaur.

I'm a tiny mammal,
So small, I'm hard to see
But dinosaurs had better watch out,
'Cause the future belongs to me.

- On the back, write about the similes in verses 2–4 following the pattern below (replace the words in bold when writing about the other verses).

Pattern

The simile in verse **one** compares the **stegosaurus's back** to a **saw**. This is effective because **saw teeth** have a similar **zig-zag** shape.

Dear Helper,

Objective: to understand the use of similes in poetry.
Share the reading of the poem with your child. They will need most help when trying to explain why the simile is effective. Discuss: *What is the tiny mammal in the last verse?*

Robin and Gandelyn

- Read this ballad, then highlight all the features which show that it is an older poem. Try to guess the meaning of the archaic words from the context.

I heard the carping of a clerk
Who told me, 'tis no lie,
The story of bold Robin Hood
And how he came to die.
Robin lyeth in greenwood bounden.

Robin and Gandelyn went out
To hunt for deer one day.
And soon a mickle herd they found
A-standing in their way.

Robin stalked 'till he was close,
And then he bent his bow,
And shot the fattest deer of all,
Cleaving its heart in two.

He had not half the deer y-flayed,
Nor eke cut off its head,
Ere an arrow flew from out the wood
And shot poor Robin dead.

Gandelyn looked him east and west,
And sought under the sun,
And lo, he saw a little boy,
Was clepen Wrennock of Dun.

'Dost know what thou hast done, young lad?
Thou hast slain bold Robin Hood;
The only man who loved the poor,
And did thy family good!'

'Now will the Sheriff take ye all
And fling ye into jail,
And there ye all will starve to death,
No matter how ye wail!'
Robin lyeth in greenwood bounden.

Anonymous

Dear Helper,

Objective: to identify clues which suggest poems are older, eg language use, archaic words.
Read and enjoy this ballad poem with your child. Highlight all the features which show that it is older. Help your child to guess the meaning of the archaic words.

Name:

Lots of legs

A **couplet** is a pair of lines which rhyme. The rhyme scheme of a poem in couplets is written: **a a**, **b b**, **c c**, and so on.

- Complete each of the following **couplets** with the second line, then try to guess which creature it describes.

A __ __ __ __
With lots of legs and a funny face
He may drop in from outer __ __ __ __ __ __.

G __ __ __ __
It dresses in a clean white sheet
And gives us tricks but not much __ __ __ __ __.

M __ __ __ __
It's like the one you've had for ages,
But this one's wrapped up in __ __ __ __ __ __ __.

O __ __ __
A horrible, troll-like, giant creature
Clumsy of fame and coarse of __ __ __ __ __ __ __.

T __ __ __ __
A creature of the goblin kind
Which under bridges you may __ __ __ __.

U __ __ __ __ __ __ __
This creature is a myth, of course,
But don't get butted by this __ __ __ __ __.

Y __ __ __
A word like 'snowman' will not do
Without 'abominable' __ __ __.

Dear Helper,

Objective: to identify different patterns of rhyme in poetry: couplets.
Help your child to find the rhymes. Note that the number of letters in each missing word is indicated by the small lines.

The creature of Croglin

Alternate rhyme occurs when alternate lines rhyme with each other. The rhyme scheme of a poem in alternate rhyme is written: **a b a b, c d c d** and so on.

● Read the poem and see if you can supply the missing rhymes.

Crouching on the moorland bleak

Like a wild beast, is Croglin _ _ _ _ _:

A lonely place where wild winds _ _ _ _ _ _ _

Like witches' cats that caterwaul.

Once, on a sultry Summer's night

When Amelia couldn't get to _ _ _ _ _ _ ,

She saw outside two points of _ _ _ _ _ _ _ –

Not lights – but eyes that seemed to creep

Towards her. She began to weep

And rushed to unlock her bedroom _ _ _ _ _

But dropped the key! She heard it leap

Inside – glass splintered to the _ _ _ _ _ _ .

She screamed and saw the figure run,

Outlined against the moon's pale _ _ _ _ _ _ .

Her brother chased it with a _ _ _

But it outran him in its fright.

from *The Creature of Croglin* by Alex Burrows

● Only part of the poem could be given here. What do you think happens next?

Dear Helper,

Objective: to identify different patterns of rhyme in poetry: alternate rhyme.

Help your child to write in the rhymes. Note that the number of letters in each missing word is indicated by the small lines. Help your child with the second task by asking: *What do you think they did next day? Do you think they caught the creature? What kind of creature was it?*

Name:

Knitting needle data base

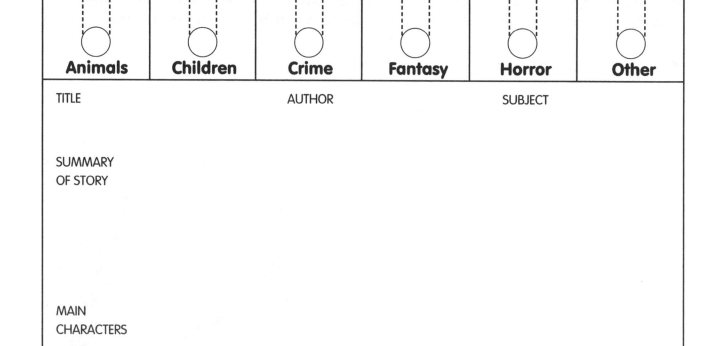

Animals	Children	Crime	Fantasy	Horror	Other

TITLE   AUTHOR   SUBJECT

SUMMARY
OF STORY

MAIN
CHARACTERS

BEST SCENE

STAR RATING

AUTHOR A-D	AUTHOR E-H	AUTHOR I-L	AUTHOR M-P	AUTHOR Q-T	AUTHOR U-Z

- Prepare a **data card** on a book you have read.
  - Write your review.
  - Cut out the page and paste it onto thin card.
  - Use a hole punch to make the holes.
  - Cut the dotted lines for the categories which **do not** apply to the book.

Dear Helper,

Objective: to review a story.

Help your child to prepare this data card. Discuss the book that they have read, and help to fill in the categories. Ensure careful preparation of the card, or it will not work as intended. (What should happen is that when all the cards are filed together, certain cards can be selected by placing a knitting needle through the appropriate hole. The needle will only pick up the relevant cards.

School setting

- Use this plan of a school as the setting for a story. Make notes for a story based on what you can see in the plan (for example: a child falls into the pond, a ghost is seen in the Old Infant School). Use a separate sheet of paper for your notes.

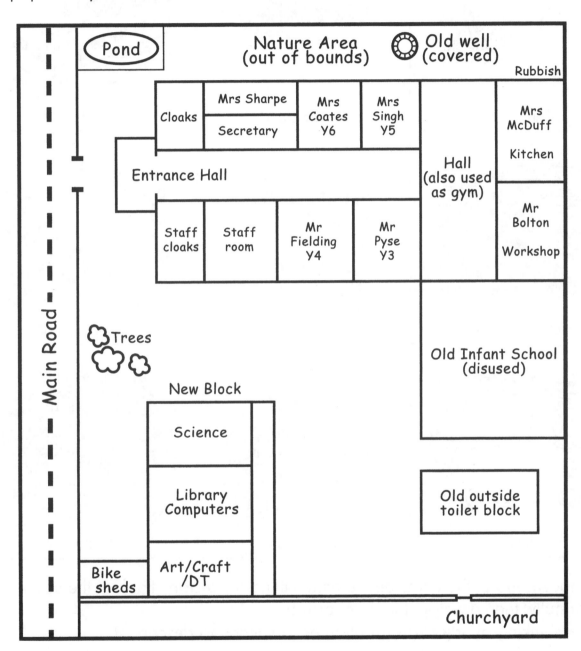

Dear Helper,

Objective: to write a story based on a specific setting.

Discuss the plan of the school with your child. Encourage them to think of incidents that might occur in different places.

Alien planet

Alien planet

Desert island

Factory

Haunted house

Medieval castle

Shopping mall

Space station

Theme park

Victorian town

- Choose one of the cards above as a setting for a story. Look at the scene carefully, then develop it in note form by:
  - thinking of adjectives and figures of speech to describe it
  - drawing a map of the area
  - adding place names
  - adding details, especially those which could be used in a story, eg a deep well. Use a separate page for your map.

Dear Helper,

Objective: to develop use of settings in own writing.

Discuss the card which your child chooses, helping them to add imaginary details.

Name:

Whale

- Read the poem, 'Whale', then write a poem about an animal of your choice by following the prompts.

Whale
Huge
Mighty
Mountainous
Whale
Diving to the deeps
Powerfully
Elegantly
Like a nuclear submarine
I would be sad if you disappeared from the earth
Whale
Mighty Whale

Prompts	Your poem
Write an adjective to describe your animal.	
Write another adjective.	
And another.	
Write the name of your animal.	
Write a verb phrase to describe your animal moving.	
Write an adverb to go with the verb.	
Write another adverb.	
Write a simile comparing your animal to something else.	
Write a line which explains how you feel about your animal.	
Write the name of your animal.	
Write your best adjective for the animal and write the name again.	

Dear Helper,

Objective: to write poetry based on the structure of a poem read.

Help your child to think of a suitable animal and for ideas for each prompt. Write your own poem as well and share it with your child.

Stonehenge

- This description of Stonehenge is 200 words long. Cut it down to 100 words or less by deleting everything that is not essential, factual information.

Stonehenge is a circular group of huge stones, not far from Salisbury in South West England. It was built around 3000 BC in the Neolithic period (New Stone Age). Some of the largest stones weigh about 50 tonnes, yet they were brought all the way from Wales. Imagine how difficult that was! Moving these stones would not be easy even with today's cranes and lorries, yet all the Neolithic people had were wooden rollers, ropes and lots of muscle power!

The heelstone, which weighs 36 tonnes, was placed so that on Midsummer Day (June the 24th) the sun rises directly above it. So perhaps Stonehenge was some kind of observatory. It is amazing to think that the people of 4000 years ago could know so much about the universe!

Some believe that Stonehenge was a druid temple, and that it was used for human sacrifice. A skeleton which was found recently may be evidence for this, as its head had been cut off. Imagine the scene: druids gather in their flowing robes, the victim is killed, blood flows from the altar stone. It is a scene of horror, but also one of the reasons why Stonehenge stirs the imagination today.

Dear Helper,

Objective: to edit a passage by deleting the less important parts.
The first step is to decide what is the essential, factual information. Pick this out and highlight it. Then delete what is left over.

Non-fiction review

- After finishing a research task, evaluate some of the books you used by filling in this form.

What I was looking for: Explain briefly what you wanted to find out.

Titles of books I looked at: List from two to four titles and say briefly what each was like (eg lots of text, few pictures, good index, etc.).

What I found out: Explain what you found out and note which book or books contained the most useful information.

How I found it: Explain the process of searching (eg looking at contents, scanning, etc.).

Which book was best and why: Give more detail about the good points of the book which you found most helpful.

Dear Helper,

Objective: to evaluate non-fiction books for their usefulness.

Discuss the research task with your child, and ask them to talk about the different books (these will already have been listed while at school).

Armour

- Imagine you are researching the history of the helmet. Highlight or underline all the helpful information in this article.
- Use the information to help you write a short article about helmets. You can use the back of the page.

Greeks and Romans

Armour is a protective covering worn in battle. The commonest and most important piece of armour is the helmet. This has taken many forms throughout the ages. Greek and Roman helmets protected the whole head and the cheeks as well. The Romans also wore body armour of mail (linked iron rings) or plates.

Vikings

The Vikings are famous for their horned helmets, though recent research shows that Viking helmets did not have horns. However, helmets have been found with metal 'spectacle' plates to protect the eyes, and these look just as frightening. Some of the richer Vikings might also have worn mail shirts.

Knights

In the 13th century, mail armour was extended to cover the whole body, and a huge helmet, called the Great Helm, was worn to protect the head from lances during tournaments. In the 14th and 15th centuries armour became more and more elaborate, until the whole body was covered with plate armour.

Normans

Norman armour is clearly shown on the Bayeux tapestry. Normans wore a conical helmet with a 'nasal' – a strip of iron which protected the nose. They also wore long mail shirts called 'hauberks' to protect the body.

Modern warfare

The invention of guns brought about the end of armour, as armour which was strong enough to stop bullets would be too heavy to wear. For centuries most soliders simply wore some kind of cap such as a shako or busby. However, in the First World War the helmet was brought back to protect against shrapnel.

Dear Helper,

Objective: to mark extracts by selecting key headings, words or sentences.

Read this passage with your child and help them to pick out all the information about helmets.

Flying machines

A **paragraph** is a series of sentences on one topic. Non-fiction paragraphs are sometimes introduced by **subheadings**. Non-fiction can be set out in indented or **block** paragraphs.

Indented paragraphs: new paragraphs are shown by indenting the first line by approximately 1cm.

Block paragraphs: new paragraphs are shown by leaving a whole blank line between paragraphs.

- Read the passage about flying machines and pick out four separate topics. Mark the beginning of each new paragraph with the symbol **//**.
- Think of a suitable subheading for each paragraph.

For centuries man has dreamed of being able to fly. As long ago as the 15th century, Leonardo da Vinci drew sketches of flying machines. However, he was ahead of his time and his machines were impossible to build with the tools of the day. Man's first successful flight took place in 1783. The Montgolfier brothers filled a large paper balloon with hot smoke from a fire, and it floated 1800 metres into the air. To the people watching, it seemed a miracle, but balloons and airships soon became common. The first flight by an aeroplane took place in 1903, at Kitty Hawk, in the USA. The aeroplane had been made by two brothers, Orville and Wilbur Wright. Though gliders had been flown successfully for many years, the importance of this invention was that it allowed for long-distance flight. The most exciting flight of all must be the journey to the moon. On 20 July, 1969, United States astronauts Neil Armstrong and Edwin Aldrin took off in one of the mighty Apollo rockets and travelled to the moon. They landed in the Sea of Tranquillity. They did several experiments, and then took off for earth with soil and rock samples. After a trouble-free flight, they landed safely.

Dear Helper,

Objective: to use paragraphs to organise information.
Share the reading of the passage with your child. Careful reading will help them to decide when each new topic is introduced and, therefore, when a new paragraph is needed.

Name:

Legend or history?

- Read these notes about Robin Hood.
- Make notes about your own opinion in the blank oval.
- Use the notes as the basis for a short article. Use a separate piece of paper.

Legend
- Robin Hood – an earl who was made an outlaw
- lived in Sherwood forest
- dressed in Lincoln green
- robbed from the rich, gave to the poor

Characters
- Little John – tall, named as a joke, Robin's right hand man, grave can be seen in Hathersage, Derbyshire
- Friar Tuck – fat, merry – a holy man but good fighter
- Allan A-dale – minstrel
- Maid Marian – Robin's ladylove – married at Edwinstowe church
- Sheriff of Nottingham – Robin's enemy, outlawed him, tried to get rid of him

Robin Hood

**Legend or History?
My Opinion**

History
- Robin Hood mentioned in official documents for Yorkshire in 1230, as 'Robertus Hood, outlaw'
- Robin Hood mentioned in poem 'Piers Plowman' in 1377
- Gravestone at Kirklees Priory says 'Here lies Robard Hude'
- Lots of ballads – some from 14th and 15th centuries

Dear Helper,

Objective: to fill out notes into connected prose.

Read through these notes with your child and discuss ideas for the empty box. Help your child to turn them into connected prose, by checking that they are writing in full sentences.

Arena

- Use the sources below (and others you can find) to write a brief history of the Roman Arena (in no more than 150 words). Include essential information in chronological order and avoid repetition. Use a separate page for your writing.

In the 3rd century AD, Perpetua was sent to the arena because, as a Christian, she refused to worship the Roman gods. A mad bull was sent into the arena to kill her. It butted her and trampled her. She was badly wounded but not killed, so a gladiator was sent to finish her off with a sword.

from Fox's *Book of Martyrs* (children's edition)

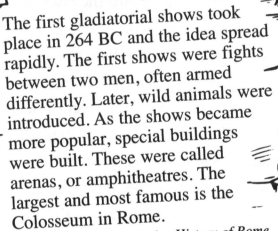

The first gladiatorial shows took place in 264 BC and the idea spread rapidly. The first shows were fights between two men, often armed differently. Later, wild animals were introduced. As the shows became more popular, special buildings were built. These were called arenas, or amphitheatres. The largest and most famous is the Colosseum in Rome.

from *A Junior History of Rome* .

The arena was a kind of zoo to the Romans. It was the only place they could see animals from other lands: lions, tigers, crocodiles – even elephants. Unfortunately, they did not share our view about kindness to animals, and enjoyed watching them being killed by gladiators. It is interesting that the spirit of the arena survives to today in the Spanish bullfight.

from *The History of Zoos*

The Colosseum was begun in about 70 AD by the Emperor Vespasian. It is elliptical in shape and is 86 metres long by 54 metres wide. It is the largest amphitheatre in the world and could seat 50,000 people. It was used to stage gladiatorial combats, which included gladiators, condemned criminals, and wild animals. On one occasion it was flooded to stage a naval battle.

from *The Architecture of Classical Rome*

Dear Helper,

Objective: to collect information from a variety of sources.

Begin by reading the above sources with your child. If you can, find information from other sources (though this is not essential). Help your child to pick out the essential information to write a brief history of the Roman Arena.

Name:

Flushed with success

- Re-write this explanation by:
  - dividing it into paragraphs (eg a paragraph for each stage of the process);
  - adding link words and phrases where indicated (see list below – you can use a word or phrase more than once);
  - adding subheadings and numbering, eg **Stage 1: Problems**, etc. Use the back of this page.

Link words and phrases

and	so that	until
as a result	sometimes	when
just in case	this	which
or	this means that	

_____ the handle is pulled, a lever lifts a valve _____ lets the water out of the cistern. _____ flows down a pipe and flushes the toilet. _____, the water level falls _____ the ballcock opens a valve. With the valve open, water pours into the cistern, _____ it fills up again. The ballcock rises _____ the valve is closed. _____ cuts off the water supply _____ the cistern would overflow. _____ something goes wrong, there is an overflow pipe _____ takes the surplus water to an outside pipe so that the floor around the toilet is not flooded. _____ the chain from the lever to the valve comes off or breaks _____ when you pull the handle nothing happens. Replace the chain – a piece of string will do for a temporary repair. Sometimes the cistern overflows. The ballcock may be leaking. _____ it will not float on the water _____ the valve will not close. Warning – always wash your hands after repairing a toilet!

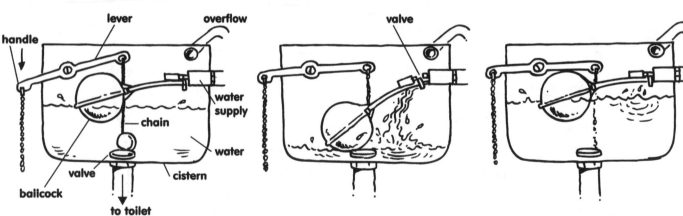

Dear Helper,

Objective: to improve the cohesion of explanations through paragraphing, link phrases, subheadings, numbering, etc.

Read this explanation with your child a number of times so that you are both clear about the three stages in the explanation. Divide the text into paragraphs. Then help your child to choose appropriate link words and phrases to fill the gaps.

Name:

Engine

- Write, in the boxes provided, an explanation to go with these diagrams of the internal combustion engine. Use words and phrases from the diagrams in your explanation.

A suggested 'starter': **The first stage begins when the inlet valve opens to let in the mixture of petrol and air...**

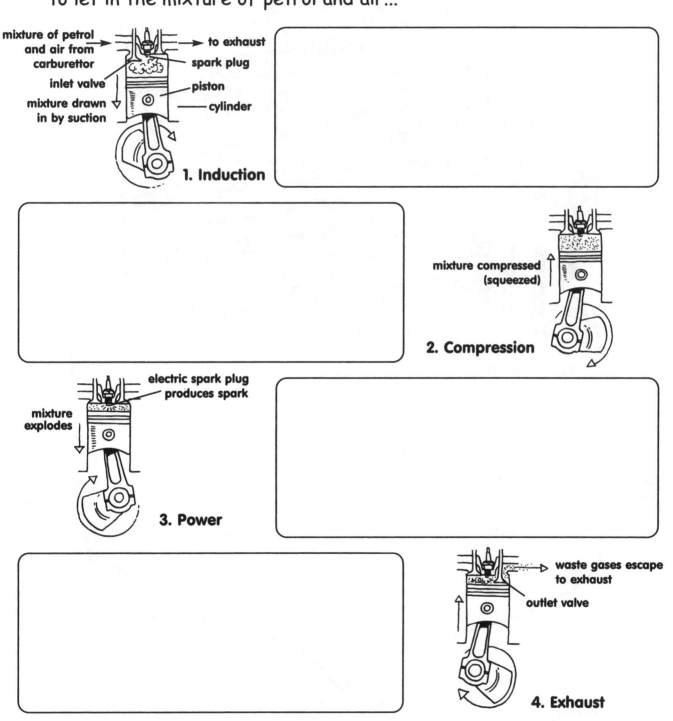

Dear Helper,

Objective: to write explanations.

Help your child to explain these diagrams in words. All the necessary terminology can be found in the diagrams.

Name:

ss

- Add **s** or **ss** to each of the following words. Take particular care with the last three words in the right-hand column.
- Find more words containing the letter sequence **ss**.

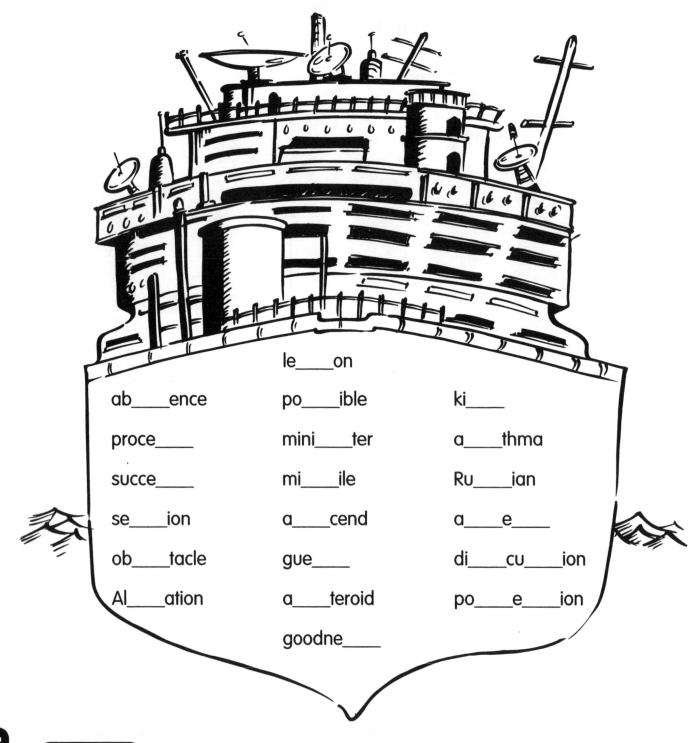

le____on

ab____ence   po____ible   ki____

proce____   mini____ter   a____thma

succe____   mi____ile   Ru____ian

se____ion   a____cend   a____e____

ob____tacle   gue____   di____cu____ion

Al____ation   a____teroid   po____e____ion

goodne____

Dear Helper,

Objective: to explore the letter sequence ss.

The letter sequence *ss* causes spelling problems in some words, particularly words like the last three in the right-hand column. Encourage your child to consult a dictionary where necessary.

From aqua to aquarium

Root word	Modern word	Root word	Modern word
aqua (water)	aquarium	porto (carry)	porter
audio (hear)	audience	rota (wheel)	rotate
centum (hundred)	century	scribo (write)	describe
liber (free)	liberty	unus (one)	unit
navis (ship)	navy	vanus (empty)	vanish
plus (more)	surplus	video (see)	video recorder

Extra words

aquatic	liberal	transport	union
audible	navigate	rotary	vain
cent	plural	manuscript	vision

- Study the root words and the modern words that have been formed from them.
- Then, cut out the cards, shuffle them and see if you can match the **root word** with its **modern word**.

Extension

- Match the extra words to the correct roots.

Dear Helper,

Objective: to classify words with common roots.
See if your child knows the meaning of the modern English words given. If not, help them use a dictionary to find out.

PHOTOCOPIABLE

Boy overboard!

In English, many words which sound the same are spelled differently to show different meanings. Words of this kind are called **homophones**. It is interesting to note dialect differences: **ant** and **aunt** are pronounced in the same way by Northerners, and **bomb** and **balm** are pronounced the same way by Americans!

- Read each sentence, then re-spell the words in italics so that they give the correct meaning. Write the re-spelled words in the space provided.
- Make up more humourous sentences of the same kind.

Throw that *boy* _____ overboard!

I enjoy watching *cereals*_____ on television.

There was a long *cue*_____ for snooker yesterday.

I would like a good quality bow made out of *you*_____.

I am sorry to tell you that she *dyed* _____ yesterday.

Are two burglars a pair of *knickers*_____?

Oh, I see that you've had your *hare* _____ done!

This *fir* _____ coat is very prickly.

I can't help until I get the *fax* _____.

London has elected a new *mare* _____.

Dear Helper,

Objective: to investigate links between meaning and spelling.

Help your child to think of the correct alternative spelling for each word. Help them to think of more sentences of the same kind. If they wish, they can draw cartoons to accompany their sentences.

PHOTOCOPIABLE

100 LITERACY HOMEWORK ACTIVITIES • YEAR 4 TERM 3

Possible...and probable!

ed	ible	ador	able
horr	ible	break	able
indestruct	ible	dispos	able
invince	ible	enjoy	able
poss	ible	miser	able
respons	ible	prob	able
revers	ible	reli	able
terr	ible	valu	able

The endings of **-ible** and **-able** words are often confused because they sound so similar.

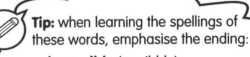

Tip: when learning the spellings of these words, emphasise the ending:

horr – ible (say ibble),
ador – able (say abble)

- Look at the cards above and learn which ending goes with which words.
- Cut up the cards, mix them up, and try to put the words back together with the correct ending.
- Make more cards by finding other words with these endings.

Dear Helper,

Objective: to recognise and spell suffixes: -ible, -able.

When your child makes a correct pair, remove it from the game so that the focus is on words they still need to learn. When your child has mastered all the above, help them to find other words to make extra cards.

Commotion and confusion

addi	tion	conclu	sion
commo	tion	confu	sion
direc	tion	deci	sion
educa	tion	divi	sion
imagina	tion	explo	sion
punctua	tion	exten	sion
temta	tion	supervi	sion
varia	tion	televi	sion

The endings of **-tion** and **-sion** words are often confused because both are pronounced **-shun**.

- Look at the cards above and learn which ending goes with which words.
- Cut up the cards, mix them up, and try to put the words back together with the correct ending.
- Make more cards by finding other words with these endings.

Dear Helper,

Objective: to recognise and spell suffixes: *-tion, -sion.*

When your child makes a correct pair, remove it from the game so that the focus is on words they still need to learn. When your child has mastered all the above, help them to find other words to make extra cards.

Is it its?

it's = short for **it is**, eg **It's raining**! (**it's** should be used only in dialogue and informal writing)
it is = the long form of the above which should be used for most purposes, especially formal writing.
its = belonging to it, eg **The dog wagged its tail**.

●   Write **it's**, **it is** or **its** in the gaps in the sentences below.

Thanks for the teddy. _____ so cuddly! I love _____ soft fur!

'_____ a nice day!' said Amy.
'Yes,' exclaimed Tom. 'The sun has got _____ hat on!'

_____ essential that all seatbelts are fastened before take off.

Dear Gran,
_____ ages since I last wrote to you, so I thought I'd write you a really long letter this time.

'Did you find it?' asked Amy
'No,' said Tom, '_____ still missing.'
'Well, I've found _____ case!'
'Well, _____ better than nothing!'

Dear Madam,
_____ with great pleasure that I am offering you the job of stewardess on Skyliner.

Dear Helper,

Objective: to learn the difference between *it's*, *it is* **and** *its*.
Help your child to understand the difference. The best way to do this is to check by trying the full form *it is* when in doubt.

PHOTOCOPIABLE

Baby bank

attack	baby	bank	beach	bed	bird
book	bottle	box	boy	bridge	bus
car	cat	chair	check	child	city
class	coat	computer	crowd	day	deep
desk	dream	ear	egg	eye	face
foot	friend	girl	hall	hand	hanger
head	heart	horse	hotel	light	man
master	minder	out	post	room	school

Compound words are formed when two words are joined.
Most compound words are written as one word: eg **bookcase.**
Some compound words use a hyphen: eg **twenty-one**.
Some compound words are written as two separate words: eg **heart attack**.

- Cut out the cards and pair them up to find as many known compound words as you can, eg **girlfriend**. Note: feel free to add new word cards to the bank to complete a compound, for example, to make **desktop**.

- Make up new compound words and then make up dictionary definitions for your new compounds, for example:
  baby bank – a place where you can get cloned babies.

- Write all your words and definitions on a separate piece of paper.

Dear Helper,

Objective: to investigate compound words.
Have fun with your child by combining the word cards in different ways and inventing imaginary definitions.
Help them to add more word cards to the pack.

Big and little

Diminutives are words used to express smallness or affection. They are often (but not always!) formed by adding a suffix.

- Match each **drawing** to its **diminutive** form by drawing a line to connect them.

Diminutives

goose

cat

kitchen

seed

pig

cigar

book

duck

statue

tree

statuette

duckling

seedling

kitchenette

piglet

sapling

kitten

booklet

cigarette

gosling

Extension

- Use coloured pencils or highlighters to mark suffixes of the same type.

Dear Helper,

Objective: to understand how diminutives are formed.

Explain any unfamiliar diminutives to your child. Help them to pick out the suffixes (word endings) that have been used to form the diminutives. Ask: *Which diminutives are very different to their root words?*

Oh dash!

Dashes are written with a space before and after them.
They are used to give a dramatic pause: eg **I tried to escape – but I couldn't**.
They can also be used, like commas, to slot things into sentences (but use carefully as they have more force!): eg **Sir Charles Cartwright – the famous designer – is on our show tonight.**

Hyphens are shorter than dashes and do not have spaces before or after them.
They are used to join some compound words, eg **seventy-six**, **well-planned**.
They are also used to show where words are split at the end of a line, eg **sen-tence.**

- Re–write the sentences below, putting in dashes or hyphens.

Many teenagers these days have an after school job.

The flowers cost a fortune but they were dead after a day!

Stephen is well known as an ex champion chess player.

Ben's attitude is too happy go lucky.

Would I ever become a dentist never!

Chris struggled with the heavily laden shopping trolley.

Rover our Alsation dog went berserk when he saw the cat.

Bill was a self taught guitarist.

Dear Helper,

Objective: to identify and use common punctuation marks: *dash* and *hyphen*.
The distinction between the dash and hyphen is an important one. They perform different functions. Make sure your child reads the explanation carefully, then help to place dashes or hyphens in the sentences.

Mandy's studio

Colons, semi-colons and **commas** have many uses, but one important use is to make long lists easier to understand.

- **Colons** are used to introduce lists.
- **Semi-colons** are used to group items in long lists.
- **Commas** are used to separate individual items in lists.

Example
The museum of Mars contained many interesting exhibits: metal from a spaceship, engine parts and a compass; broken vases, cups, plates and ornaments; and a few fossilised bones of Martians.

Pattern
Introductory clause: item, item, item and item; item, item, item and item; item, item, item and item. (Note: each part of the list can contain fewer or more items.)

- Now look at the picture of Mandy's art studio.
- Write a long list describing the three main groups of items in the painting area, the pottery area and the computer area. Use a separate piece of paper.

Dear Helper,

Objective: to identify and use common punctuation marks: *colon, semi-colon* and *comma.*

Help your child to apply the punctuation pattern to the description of items in the picture.

Turn it down!

There are four types of sentence:

Statements: It is a fast car.
Questions: Is it a fast car?
Exclamations: What a fast car!
Commands: Find me a fast car!

Do not forget to use question and exclamation marks where necessary. (Commands end with exclamation marks if sharply spoken or shouted.)

● Complete the gaps in the tables. Note that you will sometimes have to change the words when you change the sentence type, particularly for commands.

Statement	That music is too loud.
Question	
Exclamation	
Command	Turn that music down!

Statement	
Question	Are you going to France for your holidays?
Exclamation	
Command	

Statement	The King Charles Spaniel is a well-behaved dog.
Question	
Exclamation	
Command	Be a good dog!

Statement	You've got a lot of homework.
Question	
Exclamation	
Command	

Dear Helper,

Objective: to understand how a sentence changes when a statement is made into a question, a question becomes a command, etc.

Help your child to complete the tables. Most help will be needed with filling in the command boxes.

S

Only connect

● Read through this list of **connectives**, then try them out in an argument. Jot down any other useful connectives that arise during your discussion.

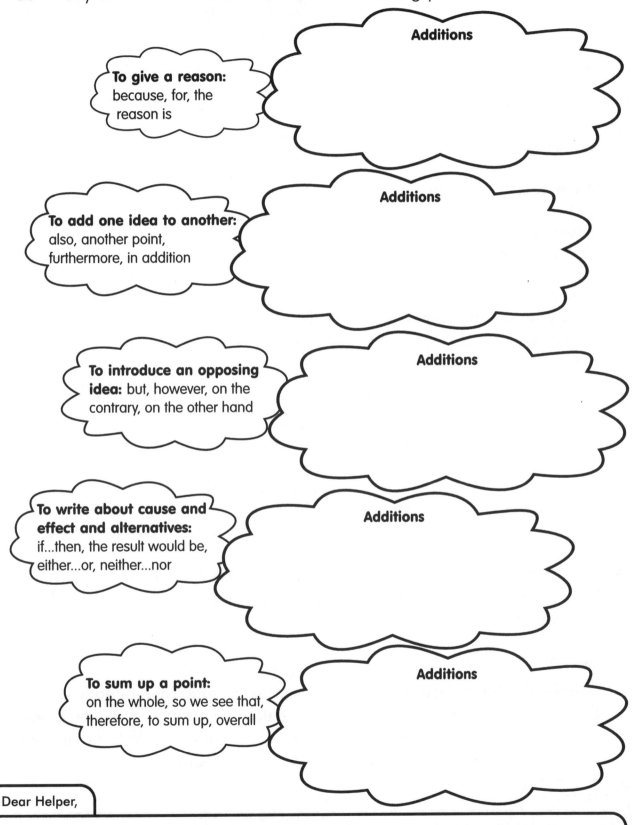

Additions

To give a reason: because, for, the reason is

Additions

To add one idea to another: also, another point, furthermore, in addition

Additions

To introduce an opposing idea: but, however, on the contrary, on the other hand

Additions

To write about cause and effect and alternatives: if...then, the result would be, either...or, neither...nor

Additions

To sum up a point: on the whole, so we see that, therefore, to sum up, overall

Dear Helper,

Objective: to use connectives to structure an argument.

Your child will have been given a topic or topics to discuss by the teacher. Discuss the topic with your child, pointing out any of the above connectives that come out naturally in discussion and adding new ones to the list.

Bina's betrothal

- As you read this story extract, think about what Bina's problem is.

'I have found just the boy for your Bina,' said Mami (Mami is the Tamil name for matchmaker).

Mother looked pleased. 'Oh that sounds very good! Tell me, what is the young man's name?'

'Balraj. It is a good name for a man. It means mighty and powerful.'

'And how old is he?'

'Twenty-four.'

Mother frowned. 'But Bina is still only fifteen!'

Mami laughed. 'True, she is young by the standards of this country, but of course, in India she would probably be betrothed already – possibly even married!'

At that moment the front door slammed.

'Is that you, Bina?' called Mother. 'Come here, I have some good news for you.'

Bina walked slowly into the room, her head hanging. Her mother's good news usually meant something unpleasant – like last year's holiday in Tamil Nadu when she had wanted to go to Disney World in Florida.

'Bina,' said her mother breathlessly. 'You know Mami. She has found you a good match – a young man called Balraj.'

'What?' shrieked Bina. 'I don't want an arranged marriage! When – if – I marry, I want to choose my own husband. I want to marry for love!'

Mami looked at Mother. Both were deeply shocked.

From 'Bina's Betrothal' by Nadeen Naik

- Discuss Bina's problem: Should she follow the traditional customs of her family's culture, or should she follow her heart? Write your ideas on the back of this page.

Extension

- Mami and Mother have more nasty surprises in store. Bina already has an English boyfriend, whom she has been seeing in secret. She is determined to have all the freedoms that other girls at her school have. Write an episode about what happens when Mami and Mother find out.

Dear Helper,

Objective: to identify social, moral or cultural issues in a story.

Discuss the issues raised by this extract. Ask: *What is Bina's dilemma? What problems will she face if she goes against her community?*

Banja's coming of age

- Read the extract below then discuss the following:
  - What skills has Banja been taught that help him to survive?
  - What are the 'coming of age' tests in Western European society?
  - How would you cope if you were in the same situation as Banja?
- Write your ideas on the back of the page.

This extract describes Banja's coming of age – he has to pass a test before he can be accepted as an adult. The test is to walk across 100 miles of desert, navigating by the stars and surviving on the food and water he can find on the way.

Banja was worried. He had been walking all day through the burning desert. He knew that he should have reached Nonang Wadi by now, but there was no sign of it. Banja belonged to the Kung people. He was short and wiry in build, like all his people, and this helped him to bear the great heat of the desert. He had also been taught many survival skills – and now he found that he needed them.

He had taken his last drink of water two hours ago and his water carrier, a huge ostrich eggshell, was empty. As he walked, his eyes swept the ground. He was looking for a hollow in the sand – especially one where the sand appeared slightly darker. At last he found one. He knelt and took a hollow reed from his skin bag. Then he pushed the reed gently into the sand and blew through it. This was to clear out any sand which had clogged the end of the reed. Then he sucked gently. He coughed – sand! He tried again in a different spot, and this time he sucked water. He filled his mouth, rinsed the water around, and swallowed. The next time he filled his mouth, he did not swallow the water, but spurted it out again into the ostrich eggshell. He managed to do this several times before the water ran out and he sucked sand again.

Banja stood up and smiled. He knew now that he would survive. All he had to do was work out where he had gone wrong, and he could do that when the star patterns appeared again at night.

From 'Banja's Coming of Age' by Jie Nalikwanda

Extension

- Write a continuation of the story. Use a separate piece of paper.

Dear Helper,

Objective: to read stories from other cultures focusing on different customs.

Discuss the questions at the top of the page, then help your child to think of an exciting way to continue the story. Ask: *What other problems will Banja face?*

The death of Robin Hood

These are words used to describe particular features of poetry.
Verse: a group of lines that follow a pattern of rhyme and rhythm.
Chorus: a line or group of lines repeated after each verse (often called a *refrain*).
Couplet: two lines which rhyme.
Rhyme: the same sound at the end of words.
Rhythm: a regular beat created by patterns of stressed syllables.
Alliteration: words in the same line which begin with the same sound.

● This is part of a ballad about the death of Robin Hood. Read it and use
different coloured pens to highlight examples of each of the terms
defined above.

Give me my bent bow in my hand
And a feathered flo I'll free,
And where'er the arrow falls
'Tis there my grave shall be.
Here in Sherwood will I sleep,
Safe within the forest deep.

Lay this sharp sword by my side,
These feathered flos at my feet,
And lay this brave bow on my breast
That made much music sweet.
Here in Sherwood will I sleep,
Safe within the forest deep.

'Twas the last time he bent his bow
And a wondrous way he shot,
And though it flew four hundred yards,
Little John found the spot.
Here in Sherwood will I sleep,
Safe within the forest deep.

Then Robin, he gave up the ghost,
And no more word spake he,
And Little John his grave hath dug
At a place called Kirkeslie.
Here in Sherwood will I sleep,
Safe within the forest deep.
Anon.

flo = arrow; where'er = wherever; spake = spoke; hath = has.

Dear Helper,

Objective: to understand and identify the following terms: *verse, chorus, couplet, rhyme, rhythm, alliteration*.

The hardest term to identify is *rhythm*. Ask your child to read the first verse with great emphasis, then to mark the syllables they are emphasising. Then, count the number in each line.

100 LITERACY HOMEWORK ACTIVITIES • YEAR 4 TERM 3

Name:

Haiku

Haiku (pronounced **high-coo**) is a Japanese form of poetry. It is unrhymed, and short! It has only 17 syllables (arranged in three lines of 5 syllables, 7 syllables and 5 syllables).
Remember: each beat in a word is a syllable, so **film** has one syllable, **snapshot** has two syllables, and so on.

- Read these haiku poems aloud. Clap and count out the syllables in each line.
- Find those which break the rule about syllables and see if you can find a way to put them right.

Out of film? Try a   _____ syllables

Seventeen syllable verse   _____ syllables

Snapshot – a haiku!   _____ syllables

Storm clouds gathering   _____ syllables

The forest sighs in the wind _____ syllables

A screech from an eagle.   _____ syllables

Footsteps on the staircase   _____ syllables

A murmur, a sigh, a knock –   _____ syllables

But no one is there!   _____ syllables

A leaf on the ground,   _____ syllables

Brown and curling –   _____ syllables

Autumn is coming soon.   _____ syllables

Two big floppy ears   _____ syllables

And a bark worse than his bite –   _____ syllables

My dog.   _____ syllables

Lucky dog!

Rhythm in English poetry is based on syllables and stress.

Syllable: a unit of pronunciation – for example, **man** has one syllable, **mummy** has two syllables, **pyramid** has three syllables and so on.

Stress: every word contains one stressed syllable, the syllable that is said with most emphasis – for example, **phar**aoh. Poets arrange words so that the stressed syllables make a regular pattern.

Examples:
Dogs don't **have** to **go** to **school**.   7 syllables, 4 stresses
They're more **for**tunate than **me**.   7 syllables, 4 stresses

• Count the **syllables** and **stresses** in the following short poems.

There's something strange about this room;   _____ syllables _____ stresses

Something that's somehow not quite right,   _____ syllables _____ stresses

A trick, perhaps, played by the light.   _____ syllables _____ stresses

There lived a wife at Usher's Well,   _____ syllables _____ stresses

   A wealthy wife was she,   _____ syllables _____ stresses

She had three stout and stalwart sons   _____ syllables _____ stresses

   And sent them out to sea.   _____ syllables _____ stresses

An antique clock stands in the entrance hall   _____ syllables _____ stresses

A grandfather in name and age and size.   _____ syllables _____ stresses

Inside its case, a man, however tall,   _____ syllables _____ stresses

Would be well hidden from a seeker's eyes.   _____ syllables _____ stresses

If all the world were paper,   _____ syllables _____ stresses

   And all the seas were ink,   _____ syllables _____ stresses

If all the trees were bread and cheese   _____ syllables _____ stresses

   What would we have to drink?   _____ syllables _____ stresses

Dear Helper,

Objective: to clap out and count syllables and stresses in each line of poetry.
Help your child to count syllables and stresses. The way to do this is to read the poetry aloud, and to beat time with it. Do not try to count stresses until your child is confident about counting syllables.

Name:

Old lady from China

Rhyme schemes describe the pattern of rhyme in a poem. They use a letter of the alphabet for each new rhyme until the pattern has been covered (usually one verse).

Oh where have you been, my long long love,	a
This long seven years and more?	b
Oh I'm come to seek my former vows	c
Which you granted me before.	b

So the rhyme scheme of this ballad verse is a b c b.

● Write two sentences to describe the **rhyme scheme** in each of the following verses. The first sentence should state the rhyme scheme (using the letters of the alphabet) and the second sentence should say something about the effect of the rhymes (for example: *Rhymes in ballads make the long story easier to remember*).

There was an old lady from China
Who sailed on a big ocean liner.
　　She slipped on the deck
　　And twisted her neck,
And now all she sees is behind her.
　　　　　　　　Limerick

Rhyme scheme _____

Effect of the rhymes _____

White canvas clouds go sailing by
Under the clouds of a bright blue sky
And then comes the spout like a white palm tree
And the watch's shout, 'A whale I can see!'
　　　　　　　　Ballad

Rhyme scheme _____

Effect of the rhymes _____

Dear Helper,

Objective: to describe how a poet uses rhyme.
Ensure that your child reads the explanation carefully. Another area in which your child will need help is in saying something about the effect of the rhymes.

PHOTOCOPIABLE

Dracula?

Free verse is poetry that does not use regular rhyme or rhythm. The poetic effect is created by careful attention to line breaks which draw attention to key words and phrases.

- Read this poem and try to explain why the writer chose to make a line break where he did. The first verse has been done as an example.

Dracula?	Explanation for line break
Dracula His bright red eyes staring at me Red Red Like his teeth Like my blood?	makes Dracula's name stand out repeats 'red' – builds up suspense these two lines are pairs and the line break emphasises this
I wish he wouldn't look at me like that As though I'm on his menu for tonight Wouldn't he prefer some fish and chips Or a juicy steak? I'd much rather he had a steak A steak A stake A stake through his heart!	
But it's too late Too late! He's having me instead! Ouch! I'm dead.	
No I'm not, I'm awake What a rotten night! What's this? Ouch! A mosquito bite!	

Dear Helper,

Objective: to describe how a poet does or does not use rhyme.

It is sometimes quite difficult to think of reasons why a poet started a new line, so your child will need help with this. Note that they do not have to give a reason for every line.

Name:

Mnemonic rhymes

Mnemonic (the **m** is silent!) means 'to help memory'. Mnemonic rhymes are a good way help us remember things we need to.

● Read these examples aloud and then try to memorise at least two of them.

History
In 1066
William the 1st
knocked us for six.

History
Divorced, Beheaded, Died,
Divorced, Beheaded, Survived.
(*Used to remember what happened to six wives of Henry VIII*)

Discovery
In fourteen hundred and ninety-two
Columbus sailed the ocean blue.

Flight
In nineteen hundred and three
The Wright brothers flew free.

Mathematics
Oh triangle isosceles:
Two angles have equal degrees.

Calendar
Thirty days hath September,
April, June, and November.
All the rest have thirty-one
Except for February alone.

Spelling
I before e
Except after c.
(*To remember how to spell words like 'thief' and 'receive'*)

Spelling
When two vowels go walking
The first does the talking.
(*To remember that in words like 'goal' and 'boat', the vowel sound is 'o'*)

Extension

● Write down any other mnemonic rhymes which you know. Use the back of this page.
● Make up mnemonic rhymes for some of the things you need to remember, eg dates in history, capital cities, countries, spelling rules, mathematics and so on.

Dear Helper,

Objective: to recognise simple forms of poetry: rhymes to help us remember things.

Share any mnemonic rhymes you know. Help your child to write one.

Death by water

- Read the story and then discuss these questions:
  - Do you believe that it is possible to see the future?
  - What would you do if you were Phillipe?

'Take off your clothes,' ordered Nostradamus.

'What, all of them?' said Phillipe.

'You came to have your fortune told, didn't you?'

'Yes, but I thought you would read my palm.'

Nostradamus laughed. 'What do you think I am – some old gypsy woman? I am the greatest fortune-teller in France! I read the whole body, not just the palm – look!'

He pointed to a chart on the wall. It showed the front and back of a man with dots all over him so that he looked as though he had the measles. Each dot was labelled.

'I can read the stars of the body, just as easily as the stars in the sky,' said Nostradamus.

'What are the stars of the body?' asked Phillipe.

'Why moles of course! I can read them more easily than you can read a book!'

'I can't read,' said Phillipe.

'Umph,' said Nostradamus as he began a very thorough examination of Phillipe's moles. Phillipe blushed, and wished he would hurry up, but he seemed to take an age.

At last Nostradamus stood up straight. 'You will be rich and famous and live to a ripe old age,' he said, 'but only if you follow the fate written on your body.'

'What is that?' said Phillipe.

'You must join the army and become a soldier. Soon you will work your way up to be a general – the most famous that France has known. But beware of water. I see death by water if you are not careful.'

Phillipe hung his head.

'What is the problem, boy?' asked Nostradamus. 'I have told you that you will be rich and famous.'

'I wanted to be a sailor,' said Phillipe.

Either

- Write a paragraph about whether you think it is possible to see into the future.

or

- Plan a continuation of the story which proves the fortune-teller right or wrong. Use the back of this page.

Dear Helper,

Objective: to write critically about a dilemma raised in a story.
Discuss with your child the questions raised at the top of the page. Then help your child to choose one of the writing activities and work with them to plan their writing.

Name:

Lost wallet

- Read the story, then:
  - discuss the boys' dilemma (a dilemma is a difficult choice)
  - explain the problem and alternative courses of action
  - plan an ending for the story based on what you think they should do.

The bus slowed down and stopped. It was the stop before school. One man got off, but Balraj and Ben hardly noticed him, until they realised that he had left something

behind – a wallet. Balraj picked it up and shouted after the man, but it was too late. The bus had already started again.

He sat back down and Ben said, 'Here, let's have a look.' Balraj passed over the wallet, and Ben opened it. 'Hey, there's a five-pound note here!' he said.

'You're not thinking of keeping it?' said Balraj.

'Why not?' said Ben. 'Finders keepers.'

'It's not worth being dishonest just for five pounds,' said Balraj. 'You could earn that quickly just by mowing Granny Smith's lawn!'

'What if it were £1000?' said Ben.

'Er...' Balraj hesitated, 'well, I suppose it's still the same! You'd better give that wallet to me and I'll hand it in.'

Balraj took the wallet and looked through it. 'Look, here's his address,' he said after a moment, 'and...what's this?'

He took out a folded piece of paper. He unfolded it and spread it out between them. It was a roughly sketched map. The main city on the map was Porto Paso in South America and there was a dotted line to a place marked with compass bearings. Somebody had scribbled near the bearings: 'Inca gold here.'

'It's a treasure map!' exclaimed Ben. 'That settles it. We keep the wallet and the map and go and find the treasure. We'll be rich!'

'Find the treasure – what with?' said Balraj. 'Do you know how much a ticket to South America will cost?'

'I'll save up for it!'

'Yeah, for about ten years! I think this map makes it even more important to give the wallet back.'

Dear Helper,

Objective: to write critically about a dilemma raised in a story.

Discuss the situation with your child. Speculate about what might happen as a result of alternative courses of action. What are the moral issues?

Name:

Are you a bookworm?

- Complete this reading review by circling the letter in each of the sections that best describes you.

1. What kind of books do you like to read?

A Adventure, animal, horror
B Comics
C Any books by good authors
D Don't know
E Classics of literature

2. How many books do you read in a month?

A At least one
B Less than one
C About four – one a week
D I prefer to watch telly
E Can't keep count – dozens!

3. If somebody gave you a book of poetry, what would you say?

A Thanks, I'll give it a try
B Has it got any pictures in it?
C I like poetry as long as it's modern and funny.
D Thanks (to be polite, and then I'd give it to someone else!).
E Thanks, I've just finished reading a marvellous anthology.

4. If a visiting author were coming to your school, what would you do?

A Look forward to it – it would be interesting to meet a real author.
B Look forward to it – we'd get off lessons.
C Borrow one of the author's books from the library.
D Ask my mum to let me have the day off.
E Buy some of the author's books and ask the author to sign them.

5. When you have finished your school work and can choose what you want to do, do you:

A Listen to a book on tape?
B Look forward to doing nothing?
C Re-read a book you've enjoyed?
D Play a game on the computer?
E Choose a new book to read quietly?

- On the other side of this page write about the last two books you have read. Give title, author, date, a short summary of the plot and a brief description of the setting and the main character.

Dear Helper,

Objective: to review own reading habits.
The quiz is easy and fun to do, but your child may need help remembering and writing about the last two books they have read.

Name:

Are you a bookworm?
Answers

Mainly E's

Yes, you are a bookworm, and just like a bookworm you spend your life digging around inside books. You are an incredible reader. Your friends are amazed how quickly you can get through a book. They are also amazed at the hard words you can understand. You will do very well at school, particularly in English. However, you also need to develop other areas. You can afford to spend a little less time on books and more time on sport, family and friends!

Mainly C's

You are a bit of a bookworm. You enjoy reading a wide range of books, though you find classic literature hard, long and boring. However, this is not surprising, because it was written for adults, and most children will not be ready for it until they are in their teens. You are not afraid to try something a bit different, like reading a poetry book. Above all, you probably have a well-balanced life. You read a lot and enjoy reading, but there are lots of other things in your life as well.

Mainly A's

This is not A for excellent, but A for average! Your reading skills are about average for your age. You read the average number of books, and are interested in the same topics as most other children. Your reading is coming along fine – you have nothing to worry about, but you could consider reading more and watching television less, and also broadening the range of books you read – try something different next time you pick a book.

Mainly B's

You are not very interested in books. You can read fairly well, but you don't see the point of ploughing through all those words when you can push a video into the slot to get your stories. You probably need help from someone who can find books about things that interest you. You will find that, if you read more, you language skills will improve.

Mainly D's

You try to avoid reading whenever you can. Reading for you is a slow process – so it's no wonder that you don't enjoy it! But remember: the more you read the better you read. If you try to read more, you will find one day that reading is not an effort anymore – and you might even enjoy it!

Name:

Skyliner complaint

- Read this letter of complaint. Use a coloured pen to highlight each separate point in the complaint.
- Using another coloured pen, highlight the connectives.
- Discuss whether you think the complaint is fair. Remember to look at the original advertisement first.
- Write a reply from Skyliner Ltd. Would you offer any compensation? if so, what would you offer? Use the back of this sheet.

Dear Sir

I have just got back from my holiday in New York by Skyliner and I have several complaints.

My first complaint is that Skyliner was SLOW! It took 11 hours to get from London to New York, though your advertisement promised eight hours. What is the point of a new type of air transport if it is slower than the types we already have?

Another point is that I did not get a private cabin. I had to sit in an aeroplane-type seat (though I admit there was plenty of space for my legs). Also, I was not allowed in the glass-bottomed swimming pool. This was very disappointing, because I had looked forward to 'swimming through the sky' as you promised in your advertisement.

It was good to be able to sit at a table for a meal, although you did not say in your advertisement that the cost of the meal was extra. Furthermore, the prices were shocking! I had to pay £25 for pizza, sausage and beans!

I was also very disappointed that the observation deck was open only for the last hour of the journey – and then it got very crowded. However, I must say how much I enjoyed flying over New York and ending our journey at the mooring pole on top of the Empire State Building.

Overall, I think Skyliner has some good points, but you need to sort out the problems I have mentioned, and make your advertising more honest. Also, I hope you will be able to offer some compensation for the disappointments I suffered.

Dear Helper,

Objective: to evaluate arguments in a letter of complaint.

Help your child to judge whether the complaints in this letter are fair (your child will also have a copy of the Skyliner Advertisement). Your child will also need help to draft a reply. Discuss the letter from the company's point of view.

Unsafe at any speed

- Examine this argumentative article about airships by:
    - numbering the paragraphs;
    - numbering each point in the argument;
    - highlighting examples and evidence;
    - highlighting connectives.

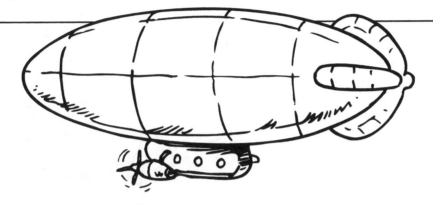

Airship Madness

I heard in the news that a new type of passenger airship is being planned. I think this is wrong and should be stopped by the government. The reason is that passenger airships are not safe. We have only to look at the *R101* and the *Hindenburg*, both of which crashed in flames with great loss of life.

Another point is that airships are old-fashioned. Even this new design will only be able to reach 300 mph – half the speed of a jumbo jet!

However, the manufacturer says that the new airship design will be much safer because it uses helium gas instead of hydrogen, and helium is not inflammable. For this reason, disasters like the *R101* could not take place.

Instead, they say, passengers will have a safe journey with all the luxuries of an ocean liner.

But the manufacturers have not told the whole story. The *R101* crashed because a broken girder tore the fabric. This could still happen, and the airship would crash, even though it would not catch fire. If the safety record of airships was as good as that of aeroplanes, then the new airship might be a good idea, but the fact is that airships are dangerous. They are just too big to control safely.

To sum up, I think there is plenty of evidence to prove that airships are not safe. You can fly on one if you want to, but I'll be going by plane!

Dear Helper,

Objective: to examine how arguments are presented.

Read this article with your child and help them to examine it as explained at the top of the page.

PHOTOCOPIABLE

Name:

Skyliner

- Read this advertisement and highlight the three things that your find most persuasive.
- Highlight anything that you think is dishonest.

Travel in the largest airship ever built

Jet powered – London to New York in 8 hours (when wind is favourable)

Safe – unburstable, fireproof	Good value – prices from £300 †

Flying will be a whole new experience. Instead of a cramped seat, you will have a private cabin*, instead of a seat-back tray, you will dine in a luxury dining room*, instead of a trolley of duty free goods, you will be able to stroll through a multi-level shopping arcade – and there's more! You can dance in the ballroom, see a show in the theatre, or swim in the glass-bottomed swimming pool which will make you feel that you are swimming through the sky!* You can also stroll on our observation deck✝ to see the fabulous view of New York as we descend to our destination: the airship mooring tower on the world-famous Empire State Building.

---

*first class only

†economy class single ticket only

✝only when flying at speeds under 50mph, and below 10 000 feet.

Dear Helper,

Objective: to evaluate advertisements for their impact, appeal and honesty.

Read the advertisement with your child and help them to decide which of *Skyliner's* features are most attractive. Help them to look for anything that is dishonest – even in a small way.

Skyliner postcard

- Amanda wrote this letter to her Gran, but then decided to send a postcard instead. The letter is 250 words long, but to get it on a postcard it must be less than 50 words. Can you help her to cut it down to size?

Dear Gran,

I am writing this letter on the observation deck of the Skyliner. It is great out here! You can stroll around just like on the deck of a ship, but when you look over the side, it is really scary! You can see the landscape like a map below, with roads like ribbons, and cars like kids' toys. We have just crossed the East coast of the United States, and New York is not far away. Skyliner will fly over New York to the mooring tower at the top of the Empire State building. The views will be fabulous! The captain told us that the mooring tower was built in the 1930s, but was only used a few times. It has been re-opened especially for Skyliner. The journey has been great! We've seen a show and been shopping – I bought a mini-disk player and an Uncle Sam teddy. The best part was swimming in the glass-bottomed swimming pool. I was really scared at first, because all you can see is sky and clouds – but when I got used to it, I felt like a bird! The only thing that upset me was the film they showed about the history of the airship – including photographs of the R101 disaster. Still, they told us that we were safe on Skyliner because it is unburstable and fireproof. That's all for now. I won't say 'wish you were here', because I know you can't stand heights!

Lots of love,

Amanda

Dear Helper,

Objective: to summarise a text by identifying the most important elements.

Help your child to pick out the important messages in this letter so that the text is short enough to fit on a postcard. If you have one, your child could actually write it on a postcard!

PHOTOCOPIABLE

T

Name:

R101

- This is an encyclopedia entry about the *R101*. Pick out the essential information for a 50-word entry for *The Dictionary of Aviation*. Re-write the entry on a separate page.

R101

The *R101* was built by the British government for the journey to India. It was as luxurious as a liner, but much faster. It had a top speed of 70 mph – three times faster than the fastest ship. After a few hasty trials, it set out on its maiden voyage, but it only got as far as France, where it crashed in flames on a hillside near Beauvais. 48 of the 54 passengers were killed.

An interesting event occurred two days after the disaster. Medium Eileen Garrett reported that she had made contact with Flight Lieutenant Irwin, captain of the *R101*. The captain gave over 40 technical details about what went wrong. These are some of the actual words recorded at the seance:

'Engines wrong – too heavy – cannot rise. Weather bad for long flight. Fabric all waterlogged and ship's nose is down. Impossible to rise.'

The official inquiry confirmed all these details. For example, the enquiry found the *R101* was too heavy and the engines were not powerful enough for the airship's size. The cause of the accident was that a girder had broken and had torn the gas bag. Gas had escaped and had been set on fire by an engine.

After the *R101*, no more passenger airships were built in Britain, though Germany continued to build them until the *Hindenburg* disaster of 1937.

Dear Helper,

Objective: to summarise a text by identifying its most important elements and rewording it in a limited number of words.

Help your child to pick out the important elements about the *R101* only.

Five-point plan

● Use this template to write the first draft of a piece of writing in which you present your point of view on a topic. Use the back of this page if required.

Make a point: state your main point and give reasons to support it.
Add another point: give reasons to support it.
Introduce an opposing point: state the opposition's strongest point and give reasons against it.
Discuss the ideas: compare what would happen with your ideas and those of the opposition.
Sum up: state the conclusion you have come to and why.

Dear Helper,

Objective: to plan the presentation of a point of view.
The most effective way to help your child is to discuss the set topic in detail as this will give your child ideas for writing.

Name:

Aviation biographies

- This chapter from a book of biographies about aviators is about 300 words long. Pick out the essential information for an encyclopedia entry (of no more than 100 words). Delete what you think is not necessary. Choose one picture to go with the entry.

Sir Charles Cartwright, famous as the designer of the *Skyliner* airship.

Sir Charles was born in Thorne, near Doncaster, on 10th December 1950. He went to Thorne Grammar School, but did not do very well. He recalls being sent out of class for making a paper plane. "It was my own design," he said proudly, "and flew better than any other in the class!" He left school at the age of 16 and joined Doncaster Locomotive Works as an apprentice. He later moved to the drawing office.

At night school, he made up for wasted time at school by studying engineering and higher mathematics. "I knew my ideas were good," he said, "but I needed to know how to work out all the stress and strains and put them down properly on paper." At the age of 21, he was able to get a better job as an aircraft designer for Swiftair.

The boss just laughed

While helping to design the new generation of jumbo jets, he began to think about the wasted power that was needed just to keep a plane in the air. He thought that it would be a good idea to design a modern airship because an airship is kept in the air by helium gas. "I took it to the boss, and he just laughed," said Sir Charles, "so I quit!"

Maiden voyage

Sir Charles set up his own company, and soon it was big enough for him to make *Skyliner*. "I dreamed of a luxury liner – like the QE2 – that could fly," said Sir Charles. "I knew it would be a hit because people are fed up with travelling like sardines!"

Skyliner 1 made its maiden voyage from London to New York on 19th June 2005. Since then, another 49 have been built, and Sir Charles has become a billionaire.

Dear Helper,

Objective: to summarise in writing the key ideas from a chapter.

Help your child to pick out the key ideas and information in this chapter. Underlining or highlighting is a good way to do this. Count highlighted words, then delete more if necessary.

Name:

The Phantom of the Opera

Abridgement: this is a special kind of summary often used when making classics of literature easier to read. The idea is to make the text shorter by cutting words, phrases or sentences, but never to alter any of the author's words.

● Abridge the passage below to around 100 words by deleting words, phrases or whole sentences. Use a separate page for your summary.

Tip: make the descriptive passages shorter.

My face was burned in a freak accident. It is horribly scarred. All the right side of my face has been eaten away by acid. I have no eyelids and my cheek has been twisted to an ugly snarl. I wear a mask to hide it. I was a famous opera singer before the accident. Now – I am nothing.

Because of my face, I want no one to see me, but I want to continue my great work in music. When I heard that a huge new opera house was being built in Paris, I decided to take a look.

What an opera house that was! It was the largest in the world, and beautifully decorated with red velvet seats and scrollwork in gold on the balconies. In the middle of the ceiling hung a magnificent chandelier which held 600 candles. The stage was big enough for a house, and the curtains were embroidered with gold.

But it was not this part that interested me. Below the opera house were five enormous basements going ever deeper into the earth. The first basement contained a hundred dressing rooms and many storerooms for musical instruments. The second basement contained workshops and space for cleaners and their materials. The third and fourth basements were empty and the fifth had no purpose but to cover up a huge underground lake.

This was the perfect playground for me. I could live unnoticed in the basements like a phantom. Yes, that is what I would be – the phantom of the opera!

Gaston Leroux (adapted)

PHOTOCOPIABLE

Dear Helper,

Objective: to summarise a chapter: by abridgement.

Ensure that your child understands the concept of *abridgement*, then help them to abridge this extract.

Name _____

Year 4 Homework Diary

Name of activity	Date sent home	Child's comments		Helper's comments	Teacher's comments
		Did you like this? ☑ Tick a face.	**Write one thing you learned.**		
		☺ a lot ☐ a little ☹ not much			
		☺ a lot ☐ a little ☹ not much			
		☺ a lot ☐ a little ☹ not much			
		☺ a lot ☐ a little ☹ not much			